D1370489

510794

METZ

PRECIOUS STONES AND
OTHER CRYSTALS

PRECIOUS STONES AND OTHER CRYSTALS

PRECIOUS STONES

AND OTHER CRYSTALS

RUDOLF METZ

WITH PHOTOGRAPHS

BY

ARNOLD E. FANCK

A STUDIO BOOK

THE VIKING PRESS · NEW YORK

Frontispiece (Pl. 1): NATIVE SULPHUR. The smaller crystal has a well-developed pyramidal habit and has its point broken off, but both crystals are on a base of limestone ▪ From Ciaciana, Sicily ▪ S, orthorhombic ▪ Scale 3·2:1

The minerals shown in the plates are from the following museums and collections: BASLE, Museum für Natur- und Völkerkunde: Plates 3, 5, 14, 19, 28, 31, 34, 37, 44, 47, 53, 64, 73, 74, 75, 76, 83, and back of jacket ▪ FREIBURG IM BREISGAU, Städtisches Naturkundemuseum: Plates 17, 65. ▪ KARLSRUHE, Landessammlung für Naturkunde, Geologisch-mineralogische Abteilung: Plates 6, 7, 9, 11, 12, 16, 27, 30, 32, 33, 35, 38, 39, 41, 43, 51, 54, 55, 56, 58, 59, 61, 63, 67, 68, 71, 72, 77, 82. ▪ MUNICH, Universitätsinstitut für Kristallographie und Mineralogie: Plates 4, 24. ▪ ZÜRICH, Mineralogische Sammlung der Eidgenössischen Technischen Hochschule: Front of jacket and Plates 1, 2, 18, 25, 45, 48, 49, 52, 57, 62, 78, 79, 80, 81. ▪ Private collections: W. Finck, Freiburg im Breisgau: Plates 15, 20, 21, 22, 23, 66. ▪ R. Metz, Karlsruhe: Plates 8, 29, 36, 42, 46, 50. ▪ A. Panzer, Oberrotweil am Kaiserstuhl: Plates 10, 13, 40. ▪ Georg O. Wild, Idar-Oberstein: 26, 60, 69, 70. ▪ The objects shown on Plates 84 to 89 are at present in the following places: Abbey of St Maurice, Switzerland (Pl. 84); Germanisches National-Museum, Nuremberg (Pl. 85); Treasury in Barcelona Cathedral (Pl. 86); Treasury at the Residenz, Munich (Pl. 87); Church of Maria de Victoria, Ingolstadt (Pl. 88); Tiffany, Jewellers, New York (Pl. 89) ▪ The minerals were photographed with LINHOF-Kardan-Color, 13 × 18 camera with lenses made by SCHNEIDER-Kreuznach and ZEISS-WINKEL ▪ Taken on EKTACHROME pan. film type B, 13 × 18 and 9 × 12 cm. According to the degree of enlargement, size of subject and lighting conditions, exposure times ranged from 1 to 240 seconds.

SECOND PRINTING 1969
ANTLITZ EDLER STEINE © 1964 CHR. BELSER VERLAG STUTTGART
TRANSLATED FROM THE GERMAN BY W. MYKURA
THIS EDITION © THAMES AND HUDSON LONDON 1964
PUBLISHED IN 1965 BY THE VIKING PRESS, INC., 625 MADISON AVENUE, NEW YORK, N. Y. 10022
LIBRARY OF CONGRESS CATALOG CARD NUMBER: 65-11372
PRINTED IN WEST GERMANY

CONTENTS

LIST OF PLATES

When I saw for the first time the colour plates brought together in this volume, I was astounded, not only by the exceptionally high standard of reproduction but even more because I saw specimens which had once been in my collection or of which I still have pieces in my showcases. I do not mean to praise my own collection by saying this, and I have no reason for doing so, as many other collectors will no doubt have a similar experience. However, this does go to show—and I am relating my experience for this very reason—that all the larger collections are built up with much the same object in view, and in the course of time, through exchange and fresh acquisitions, they all take on much the same general character. The criteria for that which is crystallographically interesting and at the same time visually attractive and impressive always remain the same.

And I would make this further point. The minerals and gemstones selected for inclusion in this volume give us an idea of what one may expect to find in a good collection. Every collector can, therefore, use the specimens shown here as a yardstick by which to assess his own standards and principles of selection, and they will no doubt stimulate him to add to his collection.

Petrographers and mineralogists will find it worth while to collect specimens which are not perfect in appearance, but jewellers and connoisseurs of gemstones lay greater emphasis on the perfection of colour and form of the stone. For him this book, which shows only the finest examples of the mineral kingdom, will have a particular attraction. But the excellent reproduction of the specimens in these plates should not cause us to forget that many pieces have been selected because they bring out important scientific data.

This is all the more important because a general text-book never has colour plates of this quality. This volume, therefore, offers aesthetic enjoyment and also provides illustrations of scientific value.

In mineralogy, the study of gemstones plays but a subordinate role, and the jeweller may well be unaware of some of the crystal forms and colour varieties of minerals known to him. The author's intention has been to show us the minerals according to their mode of formation, and then to lead us on to particularly fine specimens of generally known gemstones. Thus the book provides a link between the scientific and aesthetic aspects of minerals which should be equally valuable to the scientist, amateur collector and jeweller. The jeweller in particular, who has not the time to delve deeply into the realm of mineralogy and has not mastered the many complex aspects of the science, will gain much from this volume.

Rudolf Metz, who is a mineralogist and geologist, has very lucidly and with scientific thoroughness set down the data which will give us a fuller understanding of the structure and origin of minerals. Arnold E. Fanck has produced photographs of the greatest artistic merit. The book thus forms a very worthy memorial to the generous initiator of this project, Dr Ernst Petersen, and I am delighted to have been given the opportunity to write the preface to this work. May it prove to be very successful.

Idar-Oberstein, September 1963. Georg O. Wild

INTRODUCTION

The many fine gemstones and ore minerals which are to be seen in our museums and in some private collections arouse in the observer a sense of wonder at the intricate crystal shapes and the subtle nuances and variations in colour displayed by many members of the mineral kingdom. Man's conception of the value of individual minerals has changed many times during the history of mankind. Since Stone Age times there has been an increasing and ever changing demand for the mineral ores from which man has obtained the metals and chemicals which have formed the material bases of succeeding civilisations. Many a war has been fought over the possession of areas which contained important ore-deposits.

The enigma of the crystal shape has always been an intriguing one, and, next to the depth and variation of colour, it is this aspect of minerals which has appealed most to man's imagination. Among the sagas and folklore of most nations one finds tales of stones and crystals whose supernatural powers could bestow riches or virtues upon their owners. Often, in tribal communities, certain minerals had a religious significance, and many an ancient superstition about a particular stone or crystal has been handed down to the present day.

It is difficult to describe in words what it is that makes up the beauty of the crystalline mineral. Apart from the complexity and variety of crystal shapes, which often display near perfect symmetry, the most arresting attributes are probably the great range of colour coupled with the lustre and sheen produced by the reflection of light from the mineral's surface.

The present volume was conceived by the late Dr Ernst Peterson, who wanted to bring before his readers something of the beauty and variety of the mineral kingdom. In Arnold E. Fanck he found

2 AMETHYST (violet variety of quartz). Group of pale violet prismatic crystals terminating in pyramids; the colouring is due to minute traces of titanium and manganese, but gem-quality Amethyst is rather darker and more evenly coloured; from Schemnitz, Czechoslovakia ▪ Name derived from Greek *amethystos*—resisting drunkenness—the mineral having been used as an amulet against intoxication ▪ SiO_2, hexagonal ▪ Scale 3.9:1

a photographer whose genius and infinite care with the camera did full justice to the selecte samples.

The authors and publishers are greatly indebted to the museums and owners of collections who have kindly lent the specimens reproduced in this volume, and who have given assistance in many other ways. Particular thanks are due to Dr E. Jörg of Karlsruhe (National Museum of Natural History), Dr O. Grütter of Basle (Museum of Natural History and Ethnology), Dr M. Schnetter of Freiburg im Breisgau (Town Collection), Dr M. Grünenfelder of Zürich (Mineralogical Collection, Eidgenössische Technische Hochschule) and Dr H. Dachs of Munich (Institute of Crystallography and Mineralogy, Munich University) and Prof Dr H. Wondratschek (Institute of Mineralogy, Technische Hochschule, Karlsruhe). Mr Georg O. Wild of Idar-Oberstein has very kindly permitted us to photograph specimens of minerals belonging to his firm, as also has Mr W. Finck of Freiburg im Breisgau, who has provided specimens both from his private collection and that of his firm, Gebr. Trenkle, gem cutters and polishers, also of Freiburg im Breisgau. Mr A. Panzer of Oberrotweil am Kaiserstuhl kindly lent specimens from his private collection. — The colour plates illustrating this volume were selected from a much larger number of photographs. They show, firstly, the diverse properties of minerals, and, secondly, the variety of form and colour of individual mineral species. — This volume is not intended to be a text-book, but sets out to convey an impression of the shapes and colours of minerals in their natural form. The minerals selected for particular mention in the text are those illustrated in the plates. For more detailed descriptions of the properties, occurrence and uses of minerals, gemstones and rocks, the reader is referred to the list of text-books and reference works given in the bibliography.

12

3 LABRADORITE (dark purplish-grey plagioclase or soda-lime feldspar). Massive specimen bounded by cleavage planes, the top right hand corner showing the iridescent play of colour known as schiller lustre ▪ From St Paul Island, Nova Scotia ▪ Named after Labrador ▪ Isomorphous mixture of Albite (from the Latin *albus*— white), $Na[AlSi_3O_8]$ (Ab), and Anorthite (from the Greek *anorthos*—oblique), $Ca[Al_2Si_2O_8]$ (An), in the compositional range of $Ab_{50}An_{50}$ to $Ab_{30}An_{70}$, triclinic ▪ Scale 2.5 : 1

MINERALS: THEIR PROPERTIES AND DISTRIBUTION

1. Minerals and Crystals

MINERALS AND CRYSTALS. The word *mineral* is derived from the Latin *minare*, to mine, and was originally used to include all rocks which were obtained through mining. Nowadays, the word mineral is used to describe those materials of the earth's crust formed by the inorganic processes of nature, which have a definite chemical composition and whose constituent atoms are arranged in a consistent pattern. Rocks, on the other hand, are defined as aggregates of one or more minerals. Most rock types are composed of several different minerals; of those made up of only one mineral, the best known is marble, which is formed of interlocking crystals of calcite.

The name *crystal*, which was first used to describe rock-crystal, the clear, transparent form of quartz, has its root in the Greek word *krystallos*, meaning ice. In the early Middle Ages and before, it was thought that rock-crystal was made of ice which had been so intensely frozen that it could never again melt. Crystals are now defined as bodies which have definite geometrical forms bounded by flat faces and straight edges. The crystalline state, of course, is not only found among natural minerals, but also occurs in many artificially produced substances, such as refined salt and sugar, and metals, and among waste products of living organisms.

The crystalline form is really the external expression of the internal atomic structure of the mineral. The constituent atoms of any given mineral species are arranged in a definite geometric pattern

4 GALENA (Lead Glance). Bluish-grey cubes, with crystals of reddish blende and yellowish calcite ▪ From Joplin, Missouri, U.S.A. ▪ Name from Latin *galena*—lead ore ▪ PbS, cubic ▪ Blende, ZnS, cubic ▪ Calcite, CaCO₃, hexagonal ▪ Scale 1·3 : 1

known as the *crystal lattice*. This lattice determines the mineral's physical properties, which include hardness, specific gravity, the ease and direction of splitting, and the effects on light transmitted through it. Though the internal structure of any given mineral is always the same, the shape of the crystal is often imperfect, since the growth of crystals in nature is always dependent on the space available to them. The name crystal, however, is used not only for the perfect form, but also for any part of a crystalline substance which has at least some crystal faces and edges.

Not all minerals are crystalline. Some are completely structureless and are termed *amorphous*, but these are relatively rare among natural minerals, the best known being opal and amber. Amorphous minerals are never bounded by flat surfaces, and never have an ordered lattice structure. They usually have roundish, indefinite shapes (Plate 15). Under certain conditions, an amorphous mineral may, in the course of time, become finely crystalline. Opal, for instance, tends in due course to change into the minutely crystalline (*cryptocrystalline*) mineral chalcedony.

A careful look at a well-formed crystal with many faces gives us some idea of the complexity of the laws of crystal symmetry, which are among the features distinguishing crystals from living organisms. Another difference between the members of the mineral kingdom and living things is the range in size of members of any one species. The adult size of any member of a species of animal or plant is confined to fairly narrow limits, but there is practically no limit to the possible size of a crystal of any one mineral. This is governed by the supply of liquid from which the mineral crystallised, the temperature and pressure prevailing at the time, and, of course, the space available. The size of single crystals of a given mineral may vary from a mere fraction of a millimetre to enormous masses weighing more than a hundred tons.

5 RHODOCHROSITE (Dialogite). Red incrustation on porous limonite whose old German name is 'Raspberry Ore' ▪ From Herdorf, near Betzdorf, West Germany ▪ Name from Greek *rhodochros*—rose-coloured ▪ $MnCO_3$, hexagonal ▪ Scale 7:1

NUMBER OF KNOWN MINERALS. This is surprisingly small: there are at present about 3,000 known mineral species. Every year several new minerals are described, but, as there are also some which are no longer acceptable as separate minerals because they have been found to be mixtures or fine intergrowths of known species, the number of known and accepted minerals increases but slowly. Compared with the number of chemical compounds, of which there are nearly half a million carbon compounds alone, the number of combinations of elements forming natural minerals is exceedingly small. Even the number of known flowering plant or insect species is many times greater than that of all known minerals.

The term *species* has been borrowed from the realm of biology, where it has been used to define in a loose way a group of individuals with common characteristics which are able to propagate themselves. As no such criterion can be applied to minerals, the definition of a mineral species is of necessity even more arbitrary than that of an animal or plant species.

RELATIVE ABUNDANCE OF DIFFERENT MINERALS IN THE EARTH'S CRUST. Even more surprising than the small total number of known minerals is their uneven distribution in the earth's crust. More than half of the crust is, in fact, made up of the various forms of feldspar. The next most abundant mineral groups are the pyroxene and amphibole families, whose most important members are respectively augite and hornblende. These are followed by quartz and then by mica, which includes the dark biotite and the pale muscovite. These relatively few minerals between them form well over 90 per cent of the earth's crust. The remainder is made up of olivine and several minerals found in minor quantities in igneous rocks, such as magnetite, apatite, zircon and rutile.

18

6 ROCK-CRYSTAL (Quartz). Group of prismatic crystals terminating in pyramids, with yellowish dis-
colouration near the base, water-clear near the top ▪ From Dauphiné, Isère, France ▪ Name from German *quarzen*
—to crackle when crushed ▪ SiO_2, hexagonal ▪ Scale 3·9 : 1

To these can be added the more important minerals of metamorphic rocks, such as chlorite, serpentine and garnet, and the more widespread minerals of sedimentary rocks—the clay minerals
and several carbonates, particularly calcite and dolomite—and, in still smaller quantities, haematite,
pyrite, limonite, the feldspathoid family, sphene, chromite, corundum, tourmaline, spinel, copper
pyrites and pyrrhotite. All these together make up well over 99 per cent of the solid crust. The
remaining minerals, which include the beautiful ores that are the pride of many a collection and
nearly all the gemstones, form only an exceedingly small, almost negligible, proportion of the
crust. The predominant rock types in the crust are the igneous and the related metamorphic rocks,
which accounts for the predominance of the minerals of which they are composed.

DISTRIBUTION OF ELEMENTS IN THE EARTH'S CRUST. By far the most abundant element in the
earth's crust is oxygen, which accounts for nearly half its total weight. Silicon, the next most
abundant, makes up nearly a quarter. These are followed in quantitative order by aluminium, iron,
calcium, sodium, potassium, magnesium and titanium. These nine elements together make up
practically the entire earth's crust, while all the remaining elements form just under one per cent of
its weight.

We have only to consider the distribution of elements to realize that silicates and quartz are by
far the most common minerals of the earth's crust. The amount of any element in the crust is not,
however, always directly related to the abundance of the minerals in whose composition it forms
a significant part. There are, for instance, some relatively abundant elements which do not form
part of any known mineral. Rubidium, for example, is the seventeenth most important element,

7 BARYTES. Translucent blue tabular crystals of barytes on reddish-purple botryoidal and specular haematite, with yellow crystals of more recently formed barytes ▪ From Cumberland, England ▪ Name from Greek *barys*—heavy ▪ $BaSO_4$, orthorhombic ▪ Haematite, Fe_2O_3, hexagonal ▪ Scale 4:1

yet the only mineral of which it forms an appreciable part is the rare pegmatite mineral, rhodozite. Hafnium, which is far more common than, say, antimony or bismuth, forms no separate mineral at all. On the other hand, silver, which forms only 0.00001 per cent by weight of the crust, and is amongst the least abundant of elements, is present in a considerable number of minerals. Another relatively rare element is lead, yet it forms the very common mineral galena.

The ability or inability of elements to form distinct minerals depends upon their chemical properties. Some elements, whose total amount within the crust is quite significant, are found only as traces or impurities in the minerals of other elements. Zircon, for instance, which is present as an accessory mineral in most igneous rocks, almost always contains some traces of hafnium and thorium. Some elements are thus more or less 'hidden' in minerals, and it is not surprising that for a long time they went unnoticed. Other elements again, whose total percentage in the crust is low, form a surprisingly large number of mineral species, owing to their chemical properties. The large number and great variety of antimony minerals, for instance, seem out of proportion to the relatively minor quantity of antimony present in the crust.

THE NAMES OF MINERALS. The great diversity of the roots of mineral names reflects the development of mineralogy. Some names have come to us from ancient civilisations and the orient. Other names, such as blende, kies, spath and glance, are derived from the names first used by German ore miners in the Middle Ages. Yet others are connected with superstitions and myths, and many bear the name of the area in which the ores were first mined. Chemical composition, appearance, and outstanding characteristics have all played their part in the naming of minerals. Other minerals, again,

8 CALCITE. Incrustation of yellowish prismatic crystals of calcite with rough faces, small white rhombohedra of dolomite, and rhombohedral crystals of ankerite, on reddish stained massive barytes ▪ From Wittichen, Black Forest, West Germany ▪ Name Calcite from Latin *calx*—lime ▪ $CaCo_3$, hexagonal ▪ Dolomite named after the French mineralogist Dolomieu ▪ $CaMg[CO_3]_2$, hexagonal ▪ Ankerite, $(Mg, Fe, Mn)CO_3$, hexagonal ▪ Scale 2·8 : 1

are named after their discoverer or after a famous mineralogist. Many minerals are known by two or even more names, which may have originated in different countries and are now established by long usage. Most mineral names end with -ite or -lite (formerly -lith), which is derived from the Greek *lithos* = stone.

2. Crystal Form and Structure

CRYSTAL FORM. Well-developed crystals are bounded by a number of *faces*, which are usually flat. Any two adjacent faces meet at a straight *edge*, and three or more edges meet at a point, which is known as a *solid angle*. If all the faces of a crystal are alike, as in a cube (Plate 4) and an octahedron (Plate 78), the crystal is termed a *simple form*. If a crystal contains elements of two or more simple forms, it is called a *combination* (Plate 33). If in the combination the faces of the constituent simple forms are developed to the same extent, the combination is said to be *in equilibrium*, but if one form is dominant it may be called the *primitive figure*, whose edges and corners have been modified by the smaller faces of the other figure.

CONSTANCY OF THE INTERFACIAL ANGLE. In a growing crystal there is a continual change in the relative size of adjacent faces, but the angle between these faces, known as the *interfacial angle*, remains constant. Crystals of different sizes belonging to the same mineral and having the same crystal habit are therefore always found to have a similar shape. In every mineral species there are certain characteristic angles formed by corresponding faces of all its crystals. These angles occur

24

not only in natural crystals but also in artificially produced crystals of the same substance. Constant angles are not only present between faces of the actual crystal but also between its internal cleavage surfaces. The angle between cleavage faces of the rhombohedron of calcite, for instance, is always 105° 5′ regardless of where the crystal was found or how it was formed.

ELEMENTS OF SYMMETRY. The faces of perfect crystals are arranged in a regular pattern. This regularity is termed the *symmetry* of the crystal. Any plane which divides a crystal into two halves so that these two halves are mirror images is called a *plane of symmetry*. A cube, for instance, has nine such planes. A crystal has a *centre of symmetry* if its every face has a corresponding face which is a mirror image on the opposite side. The third element of symmetry of a crystal is termed the *axis of symmetry*. This is an axis passing through the crystal around which it can be rotated so that it occupies the same position in space at least twice in one complete turn. An axis of symmetry may be two-, three-, four- or six-fold according to the number of times the crystal occupies its first position in a complete turn, and the angles of rotation which are required to place the crystal into this position are respectively 180, 120, 90 and 60 degrees. The axes of symmetry are expressions of rectangular, triangular, square or hexagonal cross-sections of the simple form of a crystal. We find, for instance, that a flat surface such as a floor can be completely covered with identical tiles only if these are rectangles (two-fold symmetry), cubes (four-fold symmetry), equilateral triangles (three-fold symmetry) or hexagons (six-fold symmetry). Equilateral five-, seven- or eight-sided tiles would not do. In the same way, five-, seven- or eight-fold symmetry is unknown in crystallography, but may be found among certain animals such

10 NATIVE GOLD. Granular dendritic foil on milky-white massive quartz ▪ From Transylvania, Rumania ▪ Gold, Au, cubic ▪ Quartz, SiO_2, hexagonal ▪ Scale 7:1

as radiolaria, corals, molluscs, sea-urchins and starfish, and also among many flowering plants. The degree of symmetry of the crystal depends upon the number of axes and planes of symmetry which it contains. The least symmetrical crystals are those belonging to the triclinic system which have no elements of symmetry; and the most symmetrical is the cube, which possesses nine planes of symmetry, thirteen axes of symmetry—of which three are of four-fold, four of three-fold and six of two-fold symmetry—as well as a centre of symmetry. Another aspect of crystal symmetry is that corresponding faces have certain properties in common. Thus, in many crystals, dull or rough faces may alternate with smooth, gleaming faces, while striated faces may lie next to smooth ones. If striated or grooved faces are present in a crystal the orientation of the lines is governed by the symmetry pattern (Plate 12); and if foreign particles are included within the crystal their alignment is controlled by the same factor (see p. 185.)

CRYSTAL SYSTEMS AND SYMMETRY CLASSES. It can be proved mathematically that among the innumerable possible crystal shapes there are only 32 distinct types of symmetry, known as *symmetry classes*. These fall into six major groups called *crystal systems*, the cubic, tetragonal, hexagonal (with the trigonal subsystem), orthorhombic, monoclinic and triclinic systems. The most common minerals of the earth's crust, the feldspars, crystallise in the monoclinic and triclinic systems.

ATOMIC STRUCTURE OF MINERALS. The properties of any particular mineral are determined not so much by its chemical composition as by the arrangement of its smallest particles. This regular arrangement in space of atoms and ions is called a lattice, and the smallest complete unit of the

pattern is known as the *unit cell*. Every crystalline substance is made up of such a lattice of atoms and ions, and by combining the basic lattice structures according to the laws of symmetry one obtains 230 distinct lattice types into which all the many different crystal lattices can be grouped. The mineral with the simplest crystal lattice is rock-salt (sodium chloride). In its lattice the ions of sodium and chlorine are arranged at the corners of a series of cubes, so that every chlorine ion is linked to six sodium ions, and every sodium ion to six chlorine ions. The unit cell thus consists of four sodium and four chlorine ions, and the distance between the centres of adjacent ions of the same type is $5·64 \times 10^{-8}$ cm or 5.64 ten-millionths of a millimetre. Along the edge of a cube of rock-salt one cubic millimetre in size there are thus almost two million unit cells.

The determination of the atomic structure of minerals by X-rays is now one of the most important fields of crystallography.

Mineral Species, Varieties and Modifications. There are various chemical compounds which can crystallise into more than one type of lattice. These substances thus give rise to more than one mineral. Calcium carbonate, for instance, forms the two distinct minerals calcite and aragonite, and is thus said to be *dimorphous*. Another well-known dimorphous substance is iron sulphide, which can crystallise either as pyrite or marcasite (Plate 44). Titanium oxide forms three minerals: rutile, anatase and brookite; and another *trimorphous* mineral is the aluminium silicate which forms the minerals andalusite (Plate 65), kyanite and sillimanite. So the actual mineral species is determined by the atomic structure as well as by the chemical composition of any given substance. In some crystal lattices certain atoms of a given element can be partially or completely replaced

30

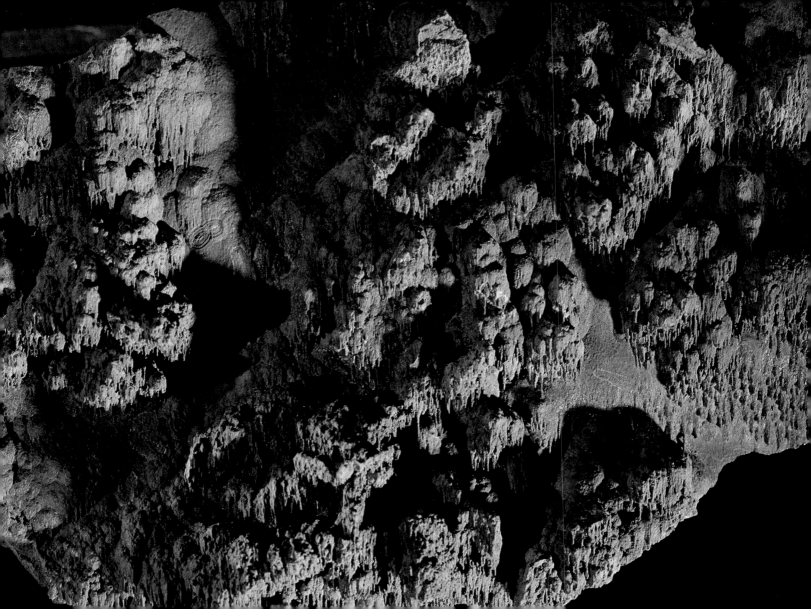

12　CALCITE　(Nailhead Spar). Colourless transparent prismatic crystals terminating in pyramids with charac-teristic striations on the pyramidal faces according to the threefold axis of symmetry ▪ From Gillfoot Mine, near Egremont, Cumberland ▪ $CaCO_3$, hexagonal ▪ Scale 2·2:1

13　CALCITE.　Sheaf-like aggregates of elongated white prisms stained orange at their heads ▪ From Cruci-mesti-Boita, Transylvania, Rumania ▪ $CaCO_3$, hexagonal ▪ Scale 1·6:1

by atoms of another element which are of similar ionic size and have the same electric charge. The substitution of atoms does not greatly alter the structure of the crystal lattice, but changes the chemical composition of the mineral. This process, which is known as *isomorphous substitution*, results in the minerals concerned having a variable chemical composition, and the divisions between mineral species in such an isomorphous series become purely arbitrary. Usually only the most important members of such a series have separate names. The important rock-forming mineral olivine (Plate 17), for instance, forms an isomorphous series whose end members are the magne-sium-rich forsterite and the iron-rich fayalite. The soda-lime feldspar series, which is collectively known as plagioclase, forms one third of the earth's solid crust. This series has as its two end mem-bers the sodium-feldspar albite and the calcium-feldspar anorthite (Plate 3).

When a mineral species contains varieties which have a different colour or crystal shape from the normal, they are usually given separate names. Amethyst (Plate 2), for instance, which has a purple hue, due to the presence of minute quantities of iron or manganese, is a variety of the mineral quartz; and emerald (Plate 25), whose green colour is due to traces of chromium, is one of the three main colour varieties of the mineral beryl. The colour varieties of the minerals classed as precious stones have been given an unnecessarily large number of separate names, which has led to much confusion. Some substances form several varieties of identical composition, but with slightly different crystalline structure, the variety formed depending on the physical conditions at the time of crystallisation. Potassium feldspar, for instance, crystallises as microcline in many deep-seated igneous rocks, as amazonite in pegmatites, as orthoclase in the cavities (druses) within granites, as sanidine in lavas and as adularia (Plate 76) in certain mineral veins.

14 LABRADORITE (Plagioclase). Massive grey specimen with peacock-blue schiller lustre on the natural cleavage surface (cf. Pl. 3) ▪ From Labrador, Canada ▪ Isomorphous mixture of Albite $Na[AlSi_3O_8]$ (Ab) and Anorthite, $Ca[Al_2Si_2O_8]$ (An), in the compositional range of $Ab_{50}An_{50}$ to $Ab_{30}An_{70}$, triclinic ▪ Scale $1.3:1$

3. Crystal Growth

CRYSTAL GROWTH. The growth of a crystal starts with a nucleus and proceeds by the deposition of layers of the same substance on its surface. This contrasts with the growth of living cells which takes place internally. In a growing crystal the rate of deposition on all faces is usually constant, so that its actual shape does not change during growth. In some cases, however, certain faces grow at a greater rate than others, and the crystal continually changes its shape during growth. If during crystallisation the material deposited on the crystal faces varies in colour or opacity, the completed crystal will have a zoned structure, by means of which its growth pattern can now be studied (Plate 74). There is usually a very gradual change in the composition, concentration, pressure and temperature of the solution in which crystals are growing, and a change in colour or opacity within a crystal is thus usually best seen in those which have taken a long time to form. In this way certain long prismatic minerals are formed, whose ends show a variation in colour or opacity. Such long, pencil-like crystals are commonly found in druses. They are often opaque at their base, becoming gradually clearer upwards until at their apex they are completely transparent (Plates 2, 6). If the supply of the mother liquor is cut off completely, crystal growth will cease. In the flat, tabular aggregates shown in Pl. 49, for instance, the growth of all the numerous needle-like crystals came to an end at the same time.

VARIETY OF CRYSTAL FORM. The number of crystal forms which any one mineral can produce varies enormously. Some minerals never produce any crystals with shaped faces, and some are

34

16 COVELLINE. Thin indigo-blue foliaceous tabular crystals covered with iridescence due to a thin oxidised skin, with small golden crystals of chalcopyrite ▪ From Alghero Sassari, Sardinia, Italy ▪ Named after its discoverer, the Italian mineralogist Covelli ▪ CuS, hexagonal ▪ Chalcopyrite, $CuFeS_2$, tetragonal ▪ Scale 3·4:1

shape of natural crystals frequently falls far short of the ideal shape. Apart from obvious structural distortions, there are other defects, such as small inclusions of other minerals, which may locally disrupt the orientation of the crystal lattice. Crystals of fairly large size are thus hardly ever completely uniform. Usually they consist of a mosaic of small blocks of homogeneous crystals which are variously orientated and may frequently interlock.

IDIOMORPHIC AND XENOMORPHIC CRYSTALS. Minerals which have been allowed to develop their own crystalline shape are called *euhedral* or *idiomorphic*. Those minerals which crystallised in the spaces between earlier formations and are bounded not by their own but by pre-existing surfaces, are said to be *anhedral* or *allotriomorphic*. Yet others which have replaced a pre-existing crystal and thus taken on its shape, are termed *xenomorphic*. Completely euhedral crystal forms are not common, as most crystals grew up from a base and so are only partially idiomorphic (Plate 6).

SYSTEMS AND HABITS OF CRYSTALS. We are able to determine the system of any given crystal by examining its faces, their number and positioning; the crystal's over-all proportions tell us its *habit*. The habit of a crystal may be acicular (needle-shaped), columnar, prismatic or tabular. Barytes, for example, can form either thick or thin tabular crystals, but both types of crystals must have the same arrangement of faces as they belong to the same system. On the other hand, two minerals can have the same habit but belong to different crystal systems. Two mineral species may, for instance, both form crystals with prismatic habit, yet one may belong to the hexagonal

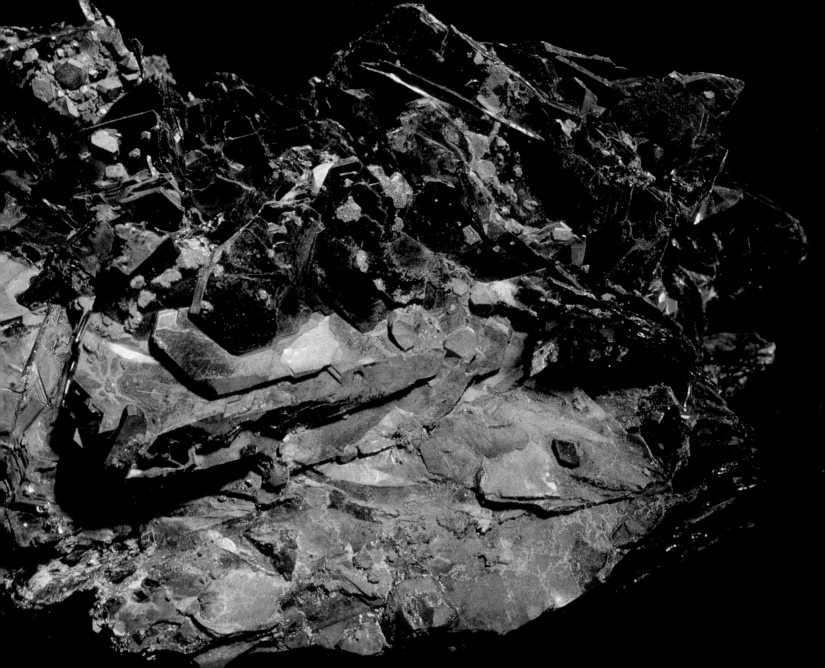

17 OLIVINE. A split olivine nodule enclosed in an outer skin of dark purplish-grey slaggy lava, the interior consisting of a granular aggregate of olive-green crystals of olivine and emerald-green crystals of chrome diopside ▪ From Dreiser Weiher, near Dreis, Eifel, Germany ▪ Name olivine derived from its olive-green colour ▪ $(Mg,Fe)_2 [SiO_4]$, orthorhombic ▪ Name chrome diopside from Greek *chroma*—colour—*dis*—twice—and *opsis*—appearance—because of its crystal shape ▪ $CaMg [Si_2O_6]$, monoclinic ▪ Scale 3·2:1

and the other to the tetragonal system. In some minerals, the system and habit of the crystal are a guide to the conditions under which the mineral was formed. (See p. 185.)

INTERGROWTHS. Both closely related and completely different minerals are frequently intergrown with each other, and many of the finest specimens of minerals found in museums consist, not of a single mineral, but of a group of minerals which are to some extent intergrown (Plates 4, 7, 8, 33, 42, 58, 68). Quite often minerals are joined together or interlocked in an irregular and unpredictable manner. There are, however, quite a number of regular crystal intergrowths which follow a strict pattern of symmetry. In these cases the minerals concerned are closely related and the pattern of intergrowth is due to the similarities in the internal structure of the minerals.

TWINS. An important characteristic of some mineral species is their tendency to form *twinned* crystals, which are strictly symmetrical intergrowths of two crystals of the same species. If more than two crystals are joined together according to the same law, the resultant compound crystal is called a *repeated* twin; and one may talk about *trillings* and *fourlings*, depending on the number of crystals involved. If twinning has taken place in accordance with two or more laws, the resultant twin is termed a *compound* or *complex* twin.

Twins always begin to form during the initial stages of crystal growth, and the pattern of twinning is determined by the relative positions of the crystal nuclei. The ability to form twins varies greatly from mineral to mineral. Some species, such as andalusite, for example, have not been known to form twins. Feldspar, on the other hand, forms twins in accordance with several twinning laws,

18 HAUYNE. Blue rhombododecahedral phenocryst showing the effects of magmatic corrosion, in vesicular lava ▪ From Niedermendig, Eifel, Germany ▪ Named after the French mineralogist Haüy ▪ Uncertain composition approximating $3(NaAlSiO_4) \cdot CaSO_4$, cubic ▪ Scale 8·4:1

the best known of which are the Carlsbad, Baveno and Manebach laws. Quartz crystals can be twinned according to a number of less well-known laws, but twins are less common than in feldspar. Many minerals are easily recognised because of the characteristic shape of their twins. Staurolite, for instance, forms characteristic cross-like *penetration twins* (Plates 72, 73). One valuable criterion which is useful for recognising twinned crystals is the presence of re-entrant angles, which are common in twins but unknown in single crystals (Plate 80). (See p. 185.)

DISTORTED CRYSTALS. If the supply of the crystalline fluid is not even on all faces of a growing crystal, owing perhaps to currents within the mother liquor, the resultant crystal is to some extent distorted: certain crystal faces are abnormally large, while others are comparatively small. Fluorspar, for example, whose usual crystal shape is a cube, may produce elongated four-sided prisms (Plate 42). Distorted crystals often take on a shape which suggests a symmetry-system other than that to which the mineral actually belongs.

SKELETAL CRYSTALS. If the edges and corners of a crystal grow at a much greater rate than the intervening faces, the resultant structure is a mesh or lattice which is known as a *skeletal crystal*. The best known skeletal crystals are snowflakes, and the nearest approach among natural minerals is the skeletal quartz illustrated in Plate 75. The so-called dendrites, which are brown or black skeletal structures (Plates 46, 47), are formed from iron- or manganese-bearing solutions which penetrated along thin cracks or planes in the rock and crystallised only after the solution had largely dried up. In shape, dendrites often resemble ferns, mosses, trees or the ice-ferns on window panes.

19 NATROLITE. Radiating aggregates of fibrous crystals with concentric white and yellowish banding, occurring in a vein in grey phonolite ▪ From Hohentwiel, near Singen, Hegau, Germany ▪ Name natrolite from Arabic *an natrum* (originally from ancient Egyptian) and Greek *lithos*—stone ▪ $Na_2[Al_3Si_3O_{10}] \cdot 2H_2O$, ortho-rhombic ▪ Phonolite from Greek *phone*—a sound—and *lithos*—stone ▪ Extrusive rock ▪ Scale 2·8:1

NODULAR AND KIDNEY-SHAPED MINERALS. Rounded or kidney-shaped minerals with a smooth, polished-looking surface usually start their life as small masses of glutinous mineral-gel. These gels contain minute particles of mineral matter; in the process of drying up they become gradually harder and in many cases acquire a definite crystalline atomic structure before finally solidifying. Of the minerals which originated as gels, only a few are still amorphous. Opal (Plate 15) is the best known of these. Minerals which were originally gels, but became crystalline in the course of time, are recognised by their smooth, rounded or kidney-like (*reniform*) shape and their concentrically layered or radically fibrous internal structure. Apart from reniform and *botryoidal* (grape-like) masses, those minerals formed from gels may be elongated and thus look like stalactites (Plates 11, 48).

MINERAL AGGREGATES. Large single crystals with fully developed faces are relatively rare. Usually numerous crystals are formed at the same time, and thus interfere with each other's development. Masses of closely packed minerals which consist mainly of one mineral species are known as *mineral aggregates*. According to their structure and appearance such aggregates may be described as: radially fibrous (natrolite, Plate 19, wavellite, Plate 49), concentrically banded (malachite, Plate 9), granular (lapis lazuli, Plate 67), botryoidal (blende, Plate 38, azurite, Plate 55, chrysocolla, Plate 52, adamite, Plate 62), nodular (smithsonite, Plate 61), encrusting (antimony ochre, Plate 63), stalagmitic (limonite, Plate 48), fibrous (malachite, Plate 54), sheaf-like (calcite, Plate 13), scaly (chlorite, Plate 76, 80), matted fibres (amianthus, i.e. actinolite asbestos, Plate 79), and stellate, i.e. fibres radiating from a centre to produce star-like forms. There is an almost

44

20 CHALCEDONY. Split blue nodule with yellowish-brown crust, weathered out from andesite ▪ From Tresztya, near Kapnik, Transylvania, Rumania ▪ Named after *Calchedon*—a town in Asia Minor ▪ SiO₂, hexagonal, cryptocrystalline ▪ Scale 1·4:1

limitless variety of forms amongst mineral aggregates. Many joint surfaces are lined with innumerable small closely packed minerals.

The form of native metals, such as copper, silver or gold, may take the shape of thin wires, foils or sheets, or be tree-like or moss-like (Plates 10, 34, 36).

INCLUSIONS. Many crystals enclose a certain number of foreign particles during their growth. These inclusions often make a clear mineral appear cloudy, or may change the colour or some other characteristic of the mineral. Occasionally, gaseous or liquid remnants from the mother liquor are enclosed in the crystal. Quartz, for instance, may appear milky, due to minute liquid inclusions which are invisible to the naked eye. Other varieties of quartz, such as rock–crystal, may contain quite large, clearly visible crystals of chlorite, actinolite, tourmaline or rutile (Plate 74).

4. Physical Properties of Minerals

ATOMIC STRUCTURE AND PHYSICAL PROPERTIES. The manifold electrical, magnetic, thermal, optical and other physical properties of crystals are to a large extent determined by the atomic structure of the mineral. Even the growth of the crystal is determined by directional forces within the lattice. If the speed of growth of the crystal were equal in all directions, the only shape which could develop from the nucleus would be a sphere. But a crystal does not grow in this way. If it is abraded into a sphere and then immersed in a solution of its parent liquid so that further unhampered growth can take place, the growing crystal will again develop its flat faces and eventually regain its original shape.

TRANSPARENCY. According to the degree to which it transmits light, a crystal may be called clear, transparent, translucent, subtransparent, and so on. In some minerals only the edges are translucent, while others may appear completely opaque except in small splinters, which are translucent.

DOUBLE REFRACTION. In amorphous substances, gases, and liquids, as well as in minerals crystallising in the cubic system, light entering from the outside is refracted equally in all directions. In all other minerals the refracted light is broken into two rays vibrating at right angles and travelling at different velocities. These minerals are said to be *doubly refracting* or *birefringent*. Double refraction can be particularly well demonstrated with a rhombohedral cleavage-fragment of the clear variety of calcite called Iceland spar. In the case of most minerals, however, the property of double refraction can only be observed with optical instruments. A mineral can be identified by the extent of its double refraction, the direction of the two refracted rays within the crystal, as well as by its other optical properties. It is not surprising, therefore, that the examination of thin sections of transparent minerals and polished sections of opaque ore minerals with the petrographic microscope is one of the most important aspects of the science of mineralogy.

DISPERSION AND DICHROISM. When white light passes through a transparent object it is broken up into the colours of the spectrum, since, because of their various wave-lengths, each of the spectral colours is refracted to a different extent, the refraction of blue light being greater than that of red light. This breaking-up of white light is called *dispersion*. Many gemstones, such as diamond

and zircon, disperse light to such an extent that they sparkle with the colours of the rainbow. In other words these stones owe their 'fire' to dispersion. Some coloured minerals appear in slightly or completely different colours when viewed from different directions. This property is termed *dichroism* if two separate colours are seen, and *pleochroism* if several different colours or shades appear. In some transparent minerals, such as cordierite and tourmaline, dichroism can be observed with the naked eye. As dichroism is directly connected with double refraction, it is never observed in minerals crystallising in the cubic system.

LUSTRE. Minerals reflect light to a very varying degree. The *lustre* of a mineral depends partly on its ability to reflect light and partly on the degree of its transparency, its refractive index and the nature of its surface. Lustre is described by terms which compare the mineral's surface to that of well-known objects. It may thus be metallic (Plate 51), adamantine (i. e. like diamond), vitreous, waxy, pearly, porcellanous, resinous or silky, to mention just a few common examples. Minerals with metallic lustre are usually opaque and often have a mirror-like surface. The degree of intensity of the lustre is thus also recorded, and we talk of a mineral being shining, glistening, glimmering or dull. The degree of lustre of a mineral is greatly reduced if its surface is covered with a thin film or incrustation of another mineral, or if there are signs of weathering. Earthy mineral aggregates always have a dull lustre.

COLOUR. Next after their profusion of crystal forms, the most striking characteristic of minerals is without doubt the great variety of their colours. In only a few cases is the colour of the mineral

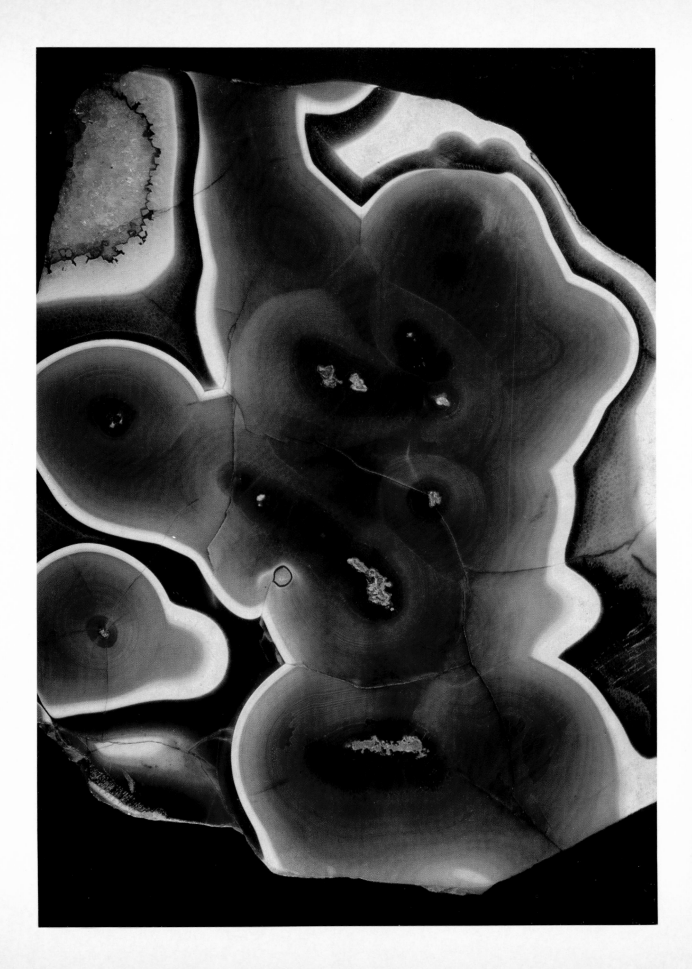

the actual colour of the substance of which it is composed; minerals of this kind always have the same characteristic colour by which they are recognised. Examples are: yellow—native sulphur (Plate 1), red—cinnabar, green—malachite (Plates 9, 54), blue—azurite (Plate 55), and lead-grey—galena (Plate 33). These minerals have such distinctive colours that the terms sulphur-yellow, cinnabar-red and malachite-green are now widely used.

Considerably more minerals, however, owe their colour, not to the substance of which they are primarily made, but to impurities, which are often present in only minute amounts. Foreign ions in a crystal lattice can produce certain colours, as can minute included scales, grains or fibres of other minerals (Plates 2, 14, 25, 39, 45, 74). Atomic radiation, too, can account for certain colourings. Minerals whose colour is due to the admixture of minute foreign particles are termed *allochromatic*, and their colour may vary from crystal to crystal. The colour of most minerals is, therefore, not a diagnostic feature. It is even possible to find single crystals whose colour changes towards the apices (Plates 6, 13), while clusters of differently coloured crystals all belonging to the same mineral are frequently encountered.

Some minerals can occur in a surprisingly large number of colours or shades. Fluorspar crystals, for instance, may be colourless, white, grey, wine-yellow, honey-coloured, brownish-yellow, pink, greenish, grass-green, blue-green, blue, violet, deep bluish-purple, or almost black. Quartz and chalcedony, too, occur in a large variety of colours.

The colour of certain allochromatic minerals may be changed by the application of heat, atomic radiation or ultra-violet light. Some coloured minerals, such as certain varieties of topaz and fluorspar, bleach slightly when exposed to sunshine.

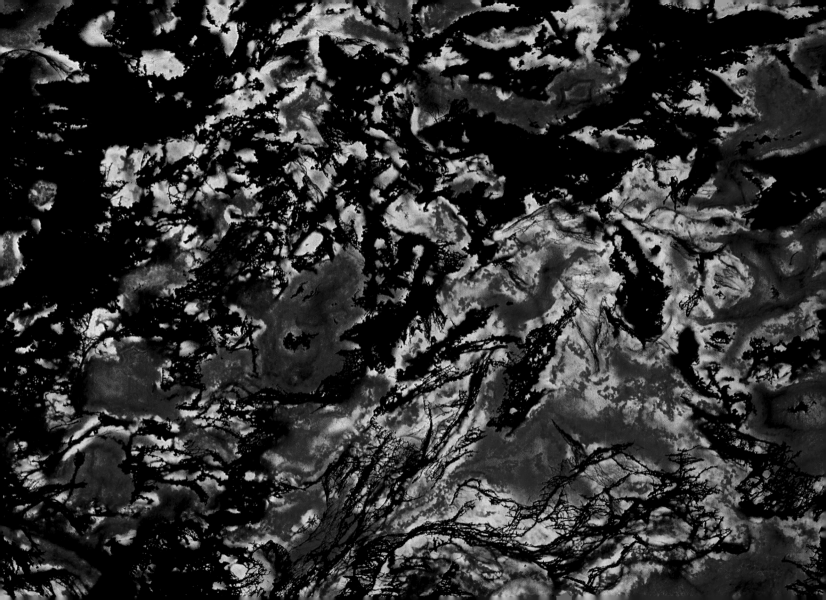

NUANCES OF COLOUR. Minerals which have evenly spaced inclusions of other minerals, or minute cracks, or are intricately twinned, can reflect and bend light in such a way as to produce a peculiar, but for some minerals characteristic, play of colours. The variety of plagioclase called labradorite, for example, often shows a rich play of colours in which blue and green predominate. The colours of labradorite change when the crystal is viewed from different angles, the variation in colour being caused by the interference of light reflected from minute, repeatedly twinned plates of the mineral which are intricately intergrown, as well as from regularly-spaced lamellar inclusions of haematite, magnetite or ilmenite (Plates 3, 14).

Opalescence is the term applied to the play of colours characteristic of opal, and can be attributed to the peculiar internal structure of the mineral through which the light is reflected. When opal is turned around or viewed from different directions, it produces a play of moving rainbow colours on a milky white background (Plate 15).

Iridescent colouration is seen on crystals whose surface is tarnished by exposure to the air. The tarnish is usually due to oxidation or chemical action by other gases, such as sulphur dioxide, in the atmosphere. Tarnish can appear on a large number of minerals and may sometimes lead to some confusion in their identification. Minerals which tarnish very readily are covelline (Plate 16) and erubescite. The latter is often called peacock ore.

STREAK. The streak of a mineral is the colour of its powder as seen on a white surface. It is often quite different from that of a larger piece of the mineral, and can be a diagnostic feature used in mineral identification. Pyrite crystals, for instance, are yellow, but the powder of pyrite is green-

25 EMERALD (Beryl coloured green by minute admixture of chromium). Long translucent green prismatic crystals in mica-schist ▪ From Takovaya Valley, near Sverdlovsk, U.S.S.R. ▪ $Al_2Be_3[Si_6O_{18}]$, hexagonal ▪ Scale 1·9:1

ish-black. The streak of the black minerals, blende, limonite and haematite, is respectively leather-brown, yellowish-brown and blood-red. Many mineral identification tables are based on the colour of streak, as this provides a simple means of distinguishing between many superficially similar minerals. Streak is readily observed by rubbing the mineral on a tablet of unglazed porcelain.

HARDNESS. The hardness of minerals has long been used as a means of identification. The scale of hardness in general use is known as *Mohs's Scale*, which has ten grades. The minerals used as standards for this scale are as follows: 1, talc; 2, gypsum; 3, calcite; 4, fluorspar; 5, apatite; 6, feldspar; 7, quartz; 8, topaz; 9, corundum; and 10, diamond. Any one mineral in this scale will scratch all the minerals which precede it, and will itself be scratched by all the succeeding minerals. Minerals of hardness 1 can be scratched with the fingernail; they usually also have a soapy feel like talc or graphite. Minerals of up to hardness 5 can be scratched with the blade of a pocket-knife, and those of hardness 7 and over can scratch window glass. It should be noted that the difference in hardness between successive grades is by no means uniform, and that that between the last two grades, corundum and diamond, is particularly great.

When minerals are cut and polished into gems or ornaments, only the harder ones resist abrasion in everyday use and escape the small scratches from minute quartz particles in the atmosphere. For this reason it has been customary to class minerals with a hardness above 7 (i.e. those which cannot be scratched by quartz) as *precious stones*. In certain minerals the hardness of the crystal varies according to the direction in which its face is scratched. Kyanite, for example, whose hardness ranges from 4·5 to 7, can be scratched by a penknife in only one direction. Aggregates

56

26 TOURMALINE. Multi-coloured crystal cut at right angles to the crystallographic axis, the colour zoning conforming with the symmetry of the mineral ▪ From Madagascar ▪ Name derived from the Sinhalese name of this gemstone—*turmali* ▪ (Na, Ca) (Li, Mn, Mg, Fe, Al)$_3$Al$_6$[(OH, F)$_4$(BO$_3$)$_3$(Si$_6$O$_{18}$)], hexagonal ▪ Scale 1:1

made up of more than one crystal usually appear to have a lower degree of hardness than a single crystal of the same mineral. It is, for instance, easy to scratch most sandstones with a knife, in spite of the fact that they consist essentially of quartz grains whose hardness is 7.

Specific Gravity. Certain minerals can readily be told apart just by weighing them in the hand. The natural minerals with the highest specific gravity are native gold and platinum, which are nearly twenty times as dense as water. The specific gravity of most 'stony' minerals, which include all the silicates, ranges from 2·5 to 3·5. The metallic ores are somewhat heavier, and many sulphides and oxides of the heavy metals have a specific gravity ranging from 4 to 8. The 'veinstones' or gangue minerals which form a large part of most ore veins, such as calcite, ankerite and dolomite, have a density around 3, and the similar but distinctly heavier mineral barytes has a density of 4·5.

Cleavage. The tendency of certain minerals to split along definite planes is termed *cleavage* and is closely related to the atomic structure of the mineral. Thus the majority of minerals can be split most easily in certain directions which are parallel to one or more faces of the crystal. In rocksalt, for instance, the cleavage-planes always run parallel to the faces of the cube, in fluorspar to the octahedron, and the cleavage fragments of calcite are always rhombohedral. When cleavage is very strongly developed the cleavage faces are very smooth and regular, and individual cleavage plates may be very thin, as in the case of mica and gypsum. The thin cleavage plates of mica can be peeled off by hand and the faces of the flakes have a pearly lustre.

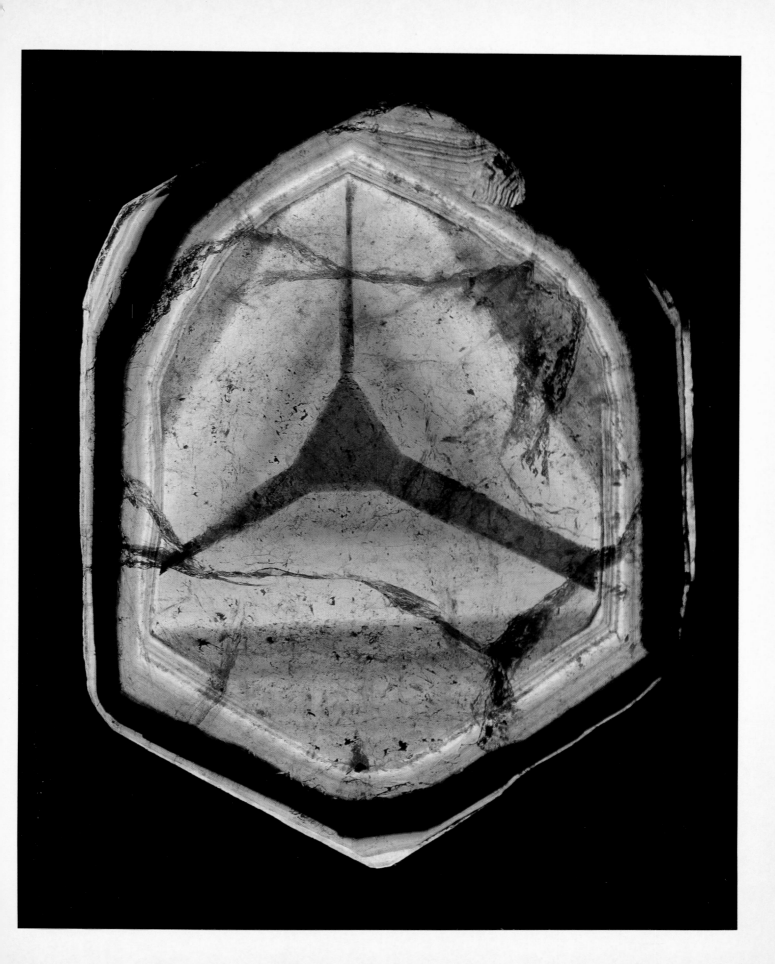

27 SCHEELITE. Yellowish wart-like crystals on a larger quartz crystal which is in places coated with grains of haematite ▪ From Schlaggenwald, Bohemia, Czechoslovakia ▪ Named after the Swedish chemist Scheele ▪ Ca(WO$_4$), tetragonal ▪ Quartz, SiO$_2$, hexagonal ▪ Haematite, Fe$_2$O$_3$, hexagonal ▪ Scale 3·2:1

FRACTURE. When a mineral is broken or chipped, it may break, not only along the smooth cleavage planes, but also along irregular surfaces which are not related to any structural elements of the crystal. Such fracture surfaces are but rarely found in minerals with a well-developed cleavage, but in others the character of the fracture is a diagnostic feature used in their identification. The appearance of the fracture surface enables us to distinguish the following kinds of fracture: conchoidal (i.e., curved concavely or convexly; vaguely shell-shaped), even, uneven, brittle, hackly and fibrous.

5. Minerals and Rocks

THE FORMATION AND DESTRUCTION OF MINERALS. Most of the sparkling gemstones and colourful clusters of minerals which adorn our collections were formed many millions of years ago and seem to us to symbolise the everlasting and indestructible. Compared with the span of human life they are indeed everlasting, but looked at from a geologist's point of view they form but part of the geological cycle of continuous formation and destruction. New minerals are constantly being formed in countless areas within and on the earth, and at the same time others are being changed or completely destroyed.

Minerals can be formed in a number of ways: they may crystallise from molten magma, volcanic gases or aqueous solutions, or they may be re-crystallised from solid material.

The rocks formed by crystallisation from magma within the crust, or from the lava which has been brought to the surface through volcanic necks or fissures, are termed *igneous* or *eruptive*

60

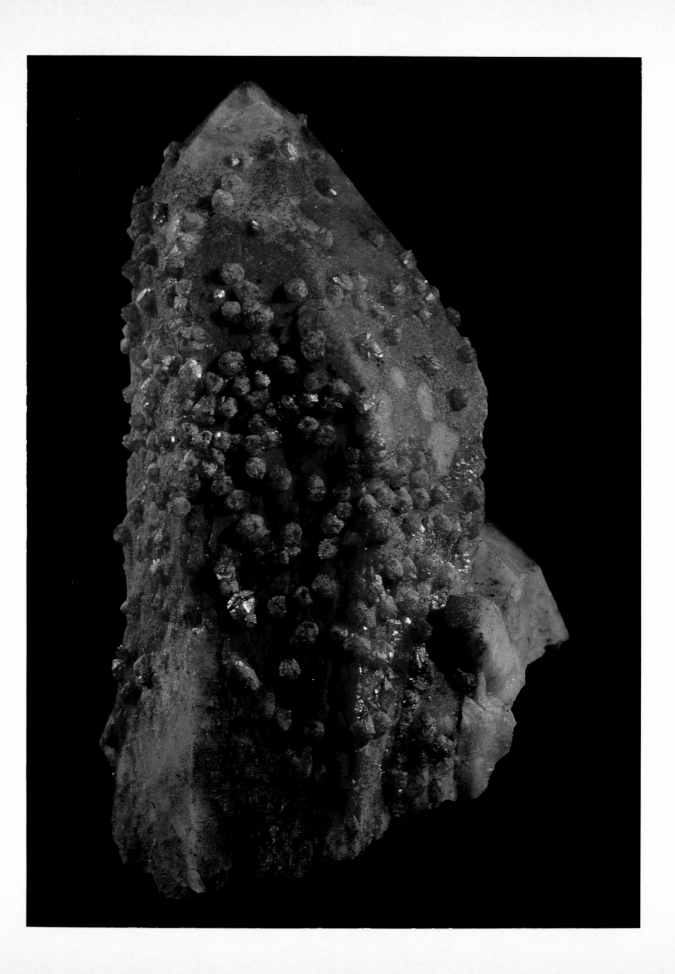

rocks. On the earth's surface these rocks are attacked by the agents of weathering—wind, frost, water and ice. These are responsible for their chemical solution or mechanical disintegration. Water and wind can also cause the weathered rock to be conveyed from one place to another. Rivers and streams carry away material both in solution and as gravel, sand, silt or mud, and the disintegration of the particles continues in the rivers and lakes and on the sea-shore. Wind can carry the smaller and lighter products of weathering; and the glaciers of the high mountains and the ice-sheets of the Arctic and Antarctic can carry enormous masses of rock debris.

The material which has been weathered by rain, wind and frost, or transported by river, sea, wind or ice, is finally deposited in sea, river-bed, sand dune or glacier moraine. If not disturbed further, it will here become gradually harder and more compact, and will eventually form a new rock. Material carried away in solution may be deposited in warm seas and inland lakes where the evaporation of water leads to a concentration of the solution. It is also used by many organisms for building their shells and skeletons, which, in the case of coral reefs, may reach vast dimensions. The accumulations which are thus formed by deposition in the sea, in rivers, in lakes or in deserts are termed *sediments*, and when compacted, *sedimentary rocks*. After their deposition, the newly-formed sediments are gradually cemented and hardened, and during this process new minerals are formed and existing minerals may be re-crystallised. Like all rocks on the earth's surface, the newly formed sedimentary rocks may again be exposed to the agents of erosion, and the cycle begins again. If igneous and sedimentary rocks are involved in the processes of mountain building, or have their temperature and pressure raised by ascending masses of magma, the minerals of which they are made may be completely altered. Rocks formed in this way are termed *metamorphic*.

29 GALENA (Lead Glance). A breccia of angular fragments of gneiss thinly encrusted with galena, in a matrix of opaque milky quartz ▪ From Wieden, Black Forest, Germany ▪ Name breccia from Italian *breccia*—crag or cliff ▪ Galena, PbS, cubic ▪ Quartz, SiO$_2$, hexagonal ▪ Scale 1·8:1

If rocks are pushed into the deeper parts of the earth's crust, or if they are sufficiently long in contact with molten magma, they may eventually come to be completely or partially melted. In such cases, the minerals with the lowest melting point become liquid first, but eventually the whole rock is converted into magma and the cycle thus begins anew. During the rise of the magma in the crust, various exchange reactions between it and the adjoining wall-rock may take place. For instance, the molten portion of a partially fused rock may be squeezed out and may re-crystallise later somewhere else; 'rafts' detached from the walls of the magma chamber may be incorporated in the magma; or the solution remaining after the crystallisation of a magma is almost complete may permeate into the surrounding rock and eventually crystallise to form veins some distance away from its parent mass.

Minerals can thus form in a large variety of environments whose physical conditions, such as pressure and temperature, can vary enormously. They are formed and destroyed in environments ranging from magma chambers deep in the crust to the ocean floor or river-bed on its surface. The environments in which the perfect mineral clusters of fine unweathered crystals are formed are, of course, much more rare. In only a few cases is there sufficient space to permit the undisturbed growth of large crystals, as the simultaneous formation of many crystals in a fluid uses up the material so quickly that perfect crystals do not have time to form.

MINERAL ASSOCIATIONS. It is comparatively rare to find a single mineral forming large geologically separate masses; but though a given rock type or mineral vein usually contains several different minerals, these are always more or less the same throughout the world. Only the relative

64

proportions of the different minerals vary in accordance with the physical conditions that prevailed during their formation. Minerals which were formed together at the same time are called *paragenetic* or associated minerals. Some mineral associations may occupy many square miles of the earth's surface. Granite, the most common deep-seated igneous rock, which is composed of orthoclase, plagioclase, quartz and biotite, forms large parts of the earth's surface. Other mineral associations, again, are found in only a few isolated localities, as, for instance, emerald associated with mica-schist (Plate 25). Finally, some rock formations result from conditions which are, as far as we can tell, virtually unique, and thus produce extremely rare mineral associations.

Certain mineral types are present in many mineral assemblages—quartz, calcite, and pyrite, for instance. Thus minerals like pyrite, which are equally at home in igneous, sedimentary and metamorphic rocks, do not signify any particular mode of formation. Other minerals, again, can only be formed under a very restricted range of temperature and pressure, or require the presence of particular minerals in the adjoining rock or the crystallising solution. The presence of such minerals is thus confined to very specific areas and mineral associations. But in areas where ideal conditions prevailed, minerals which are usually very rare may be found in quite large quantities. The mineral assemblages which are formed under the same physical conditions are usually composed of a certain definite set of elements, and may also contain distinctive trace elements. The associated minerals in any given locality are thus never brought together just by chance alone, and the number of possible mineral associations is limited.

Minerals from which metals or other useful elements are extracted are termed *ores*, and those small portions in the earth's crust in which ores or other useful minerals are concentrated are

31 NATIVE COPPER. Dendritic aggregate of distorted cubes and octahedra ▪ From Lake Superior, Michigan, U.S.A. ▪ Name from Latin *cuprum*, originally *aes cyprium*—Cyprus ore—due to its early exploitation in Cyprus ▪ Cu, cubic ▪ Scale 1·9:1

called *ore deposits*. In these areas the processes of mineral formation were particularly intense or took place over an extended period of time.

SYNGENETIC AND EPIGENETIC MINERALS. If a group of minerals was formed at the same time as the rocks in which they are enclosed, they are said to be *syngenetic*. There are other minerals which were formed later—sometimes several geological periods later—than the surrounding rock. Such mineral assemblages as, for instance, ore veins in an unrelated host rock, are termed *epigenetic*. The study of the origin, composition and subsequent alteration of rocks and mineral deposits is an important part of both petrology and economic geology.

THE PROCESSES OF MINERAL FORMATION

In the text-books of mineralogy, minerals are usually classed according to their chemical composition and atomic structure. The plates in this book are arranged in such a way that minerals with a common mode of origin are grouped together. They are thus grouped in the first place, according to origin, into igneous, sedimentary and metamorphic minerals. Minerals which are closely related chemically, or whose atomic structure is very much alike, are often shown in quite different parts of the book, and some of the minerals appear more than once. This arrangement is intended to bring out the fact that no mineral is ever formed in isolation, and that the association of certain mineral species is governed by physical and chemical laws.

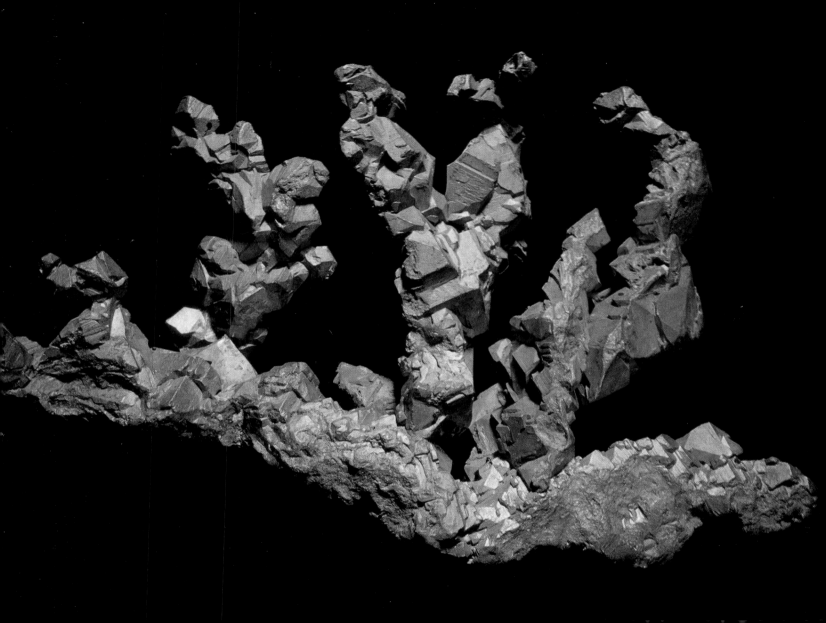

32 NATIVE ARSENIC. Botryoidal mass with concentric layers, in places encrusted with yellow realgar and associated with pinkish massive calcite ▪ From Příbram, Bohemia, Czechoslovakia ▪ Name arsenic derived from Greek *arsenikon*—strong—because it was used as a strengthening tonic ▪ As, hexagonal ▪ Name realgar derived from Arabic *rehj al-ghār* ▪ As_4S_4, monoclinic ▪ Calcite, $CaCO_3$, hexagonal ▪ Scale 2·3 : 1

We shall now consider the major processes within the earth's crust which lead to the formation and metamorphism of rocks, so as to obtain an insight into the conditions under which the fine mineral specimens and well-shaped crystals which adorn our collections were formed.

1. Igneous Minerals

The term *magma* is used to describe the molten rock material within the earth's crust which eventually consolidates to become igneous rock. If the magma crystallises in the deeper parts of the crust, the resulting rock is termed *plutonic*. If the magma pushes its way up to the surface through cracks or along volcanic vents, it forms lava flows which consolidate into *volcanic* or *extrusive* rocks. The crystallisation of minerals in lava takes place at temperatures ranging from 1100° C down to 700° C.

The igneous and closely related metamorphic rocks contain only a relatively small proportion of the total number of known minerals, but they form, nevertheless, by far the greater part of the earth's crust. It is estimated that they make up about 95 per cent of the volume of the upper 10 miles of the crust.

The crystallisation of magma into plutonic rocks at depth takes place in a number of fairly well defined stages. The earliest minerals to crystallise are those with the highest melting point. These include minerals containing the elements titanium, phosphorus, chromium, vanadium, platinum and other elements related to platinum. The most important minerals in this class are magnetite, titaniferous magnetite, ilmenite, rutile, chromite, spinel and native platinum. Titanium ores are

33 GALENA (Lead Glance). Crystals with cubic, octahedral and rhombododecahedral faces associated with brass-yellow chalcopyrite, rhombohedra of translucent brown siderite, and on the top encrusting bournonite ▪ From Neudorf, near Harzgerode, Harz Mountains, Germany ▪ Galena, PbS, cubic ▪ Chalcopyrite, $CuFeS_2$, tetragonal ▪ Name siderite from Greek *sideros*—iron ▪ $FeCO_3$, hexagonal ▪ Bournonite named after the French crystallographer Bournon ▪ $PbCuSbS_3$, orthorhombic ▪ Scale 1·7: 1

concentrated in this way in enormous ore-bodies, which rank among the largest and best known ore-fields in the world. Pyrrhotite, copper pyrites and other sulphide ores may separate from the magma at an early stage to form irregular bodies which may also give rise to substantial ore deposits. In magmas very rich in iron and phosphorus, the iron may separate out early and sink to the bottom of the magma chamber to form large masses of magnetite with apatite. The mineral assemblages formed during early crystallisation are invariably characterised by an abundance of iron and magnesium ores and a scarcity of silica—feldspar often being completely absent. It is possible to get a number of more or less distinct mineral assemblages if, during the early stages of crystallisation, the liquid magma is squeezed out of the mesh of crystals and moves elsewhere to crystallise into a separate igneous body.

Cavities or druses containing well-formed crystals are not usually found in the mineral assemblages formed during the early stages of the crystallisation of a magma, as during that period pressures are high and cavities cannot be formed. At this stage the temperature of the magma sinks very slowly, and conditions are just right for the growth of large, well-shaped crystals.

Diamonds are found in certain rocks with a very low silica content which crystallised near or below the base of the earth's crust and which have been brought to the surface through volcanic necks. Diamonds do not occur in ordinary plutonic rocks, as they need extremely high pressures for their formation.

As the temperature in the magma decreases, the stage of early crystallisation is succeeded by the main phase, when all the more characteristic minerals of igneous rocks are formed.

As a general rule, the size of the crystals of individual minerals depends on the speed of crystalli-

sation, the largest being formed when this is very slow. Plutonic rocks which crystallise from a very slowly cooling magma are thus usually very coarsely grained. The high pressure within the deep-seated magma chamber and the great thickness of overlying rocks prevent the escape of the gases which are dissolved in the magma and are set free during crystallisation.

Volcanic rocks are formed by the crystallisation of magma at the surface. In these rocks individual crystals are usually small, and quite often it is not possible to distinguish separate crystals with the naked eye. These fine-grained volcanic rocks, which include the basalt lavas covering large portions of the earth's crust, are thus often devoid of large well-formed minerals likely to attract the collector.

There are some volcanic rocks, however, which contain large crystals with well-developed crystal shapes set in a fine-grained ground-mass. These large crystals are termed *phenocrysts*, and the rock containing them is called *porphyritic*. Phenocrysts crystallised slowly while the magma was still in its original chamber within the crust. They were then brought up to the surface, where the remaining magma crystallised very rapidly to form a fine-grained ground-mass.

Magmas rich in gases and other volatile constituents often break up explosively when they reach the surface, forming bombs and lapilli as well as volcanic ash and dust. The deposit formed from these volcanic particles is called *tuff* or, if the fragments are large, *agglomerate*.

There is a group of rocks with characteristics intermediate between those of the plutonic and volcanic types. These are known as *hypabyssal rocks*, and they were formed by the crystallisation of magma which penetrated along fissures and joints in the crust and consolidated before reaching the surface. Hypabyssal rocks are thus commonly found in dykes and sills. Along their junction with

the adjoining rock they usually have a fine-grained or even glassy margin which is known as a *selvage*.

If the cooling of a lava is extremely rapid, it may not have time to crystallise at all but will consolidate as a *volcanic glass*. Volcanic glasses are usually found among lavas rich in silica, the best known being obsidian, a glass of granitic composition, and pumice stone, which is highly vesicular and sponge-like. Natural glasses are never found among the plutonic rocks, these having consolidated very slowly. Glassy materials, like obsidian and pitchstone, are not minerals but super-cooled rock melts of variable chemical composition. In the rapidly cooled, acid volcanic glasses one usually finds small skeleton-like incipient crystals, known as crystallites. These may be in the form of minute rods or globules, and are the nuclei of crystals which were not able to form because of the rapid cooling. In the course of geological time, however, natural glasses usually become crystalline, and all known natural glasses are of relatively recent formation.

Among all the known igneous rocks formed throughout geological time, two are by far the most abundant—*granite* and *basalt*. Basalt is the most common volcanic rock, and is formed from magma which has come to the surface rapidly, usually from a great depth. Among plutonic rocks, however, granites and related rock types predominate. Many granites were formed in the roots of the great mountain chains, and now crop out over large areas on all the continents. The great variety of the remaining igneous rocks is due not so much to variations in the original composition of magmas as to a physical and chemical process during crystallisation, known as *crystallisation differentiation*. The crystals of high specific gravity which were formed early, sink to the bottom of the magma chamber, while lighter ones rise up through the magma, often giving the resultant

mass of igneous rock a rudely layered aspect. Some of the early crystals may, however, be partially or completely re-melted during a later stage in the process of crystallisation, as the chemical composition of the residual magmatic fluid is constantly changing.

The first mineral to crystallise during the main phase of crystallisation of magma is *olivine*, so called because of its olive-green colour. In some volcanoes, nodules of olivine surrounded by a crust of volcanic rock are ejected as volcanic bombs (Plate 17). Such olivine nodules comprise a mass of tightly intergrown crystals of olivine of irregular shape in which are interspersed a few small crystals of emerald-green chrome diopside.

The minerals which are the major constituents of igneous rocks can be readily divided into dark or *melanocratic* minerals, rich in iron and magnesium, and light or *leucocratic* minerals, which contain a high percentage of silicon and aluminium. The most important melanocratic minerals in the igneous rocks are *olivine*, the *augite* and *hornblende* families, and the dark mica *biotite*. Chief among the leucocratic minerals are the *feldspars* and *quartz*. The classification of igneous rocks is based not only on the grain size of the constituent minerals but also on the relative abundance of the above-mentioned rock-forming minerals. Apart from these, there are also a number of minerals which occur in smaller quantities in igneous rocks. Those which are always present in very small quantities are termed *accessory minerals*.

Igneous rocks such as granite, with a high percentage (over 65%) of silica, are called *acid rocks*. Most acid igneous rocks mostly contain free quartz, sometimes in considerable amounts. Rocks with a somewhat lower percentage of silica (55% to 65%) are termed *intermediate rocks*. Finally, those rocks with less than 55% silica are known as *basic rocks*. The most abundant basic igneous rock is basalt.

Certain basic igneous rocks contain, in the place of feldspars, minerals known as *feldspathoids*. The most common members of this group are leucite, nepheline, sodalite, nosean and hauyne. As feldspathoids with added silica would form feldspars, they occur only in rocks devoid of free quartz. In certain rocks leucite forms near-perfect crystals with many faces (most commonly 24), which may reach the size of a cherry. More commonly, however, leucite, like the other feldspathoids, is intergrown with other minerals. Crystals of hauyne do, in certain rocks, have some poorly developed, partially re-melted faces and edges, as crystals of this mineral that were formed early are often partly re-melted during a later stage in the crystallisation of the magma (Plate 18). Whereas the individual crystals of plutonic rocks formed in a motionless medium show no preferred orientation, the crystals of extrusive rocks often exhibit a parallel alignment which is known as *flow structure*, and which follows the direction of flow of the consolidating lava. The aligned elongated crystals in such a lava may be compared to tree trunks being floated down a river. In plutonic rocks, the order of crystallisation of the various minerals depends to some extent on the composition of the original magma. In the case of the granitic rocks, the first minerals to crystallise are the accessory minerals, which usually form very small crystals. These include zircon, magnetite, ilmenite, haematite, rutile and the phosphorus mineral apatite. Next come hornblende and biotite, followed by feldspar. The last mineral to crystallise is quartz, which fills the spaces left between the crystals of minerals formed earlier. Free quartz is present only in acid rocks rich in silica. In other crystalline rocks, silicon is present only in the form of silicate minerals such as feldspar. The minerals crystallising first are those most likely to have their own crystal shape. The most abundant minerals of igneous rocks are the *plagioclase feldspars*, and as such they are

38 SPHALERITE (Blende). Polished section of finely fibrous botryoidal mass of blende, the variations in colour of the concentric bands due to intergrowth with wurtzite and some galena ▪ From Stolberg, near Aachen, Germany ▪ Blende, ZnS, cubic ▪ Wurtzite named after the Alsatian chemist Wurtz ▪ ZnS, hexagonal ▪ Galena, PbS, cubic ▪ Scale 1·5:1

largely responsible for the characteristics of igneous rocks. The plagioclase series is an isomorphous mixture of the two end members, albite (sodium-aluminium silicate) and anorthite (calcium-aluminium silicate), and contains the following intermediate members arranged in order of increasing calcium content: oligoclase, andesine, labradorite (Plates 3, 14) and bytownite. Which of these forms of plagioclase will be present in a given rock is determined by the chemical composition of the original magma. The exact nomenclature of many igneous rocks is largely based on the amount and variety of the feldspar present. In the coarser-grained plutonic rocks potassium feldspar usually occurs in the form of orthoclase, but in the fine-grained rapidly crystallised extrusive rocks it is usually a glassy mineral called sanidine.

If the temperature during crystallisation is greater than 573° C, quartz crystallises as a high-temperature form known as β-quartz; this can be recognised by its stocky crystals, which show a combination of the hexagonal prism and pyramid. These crystals commonly occur as phenocrysts in acid extrusive and hypabyssal rocks, such as rhyolite and quartz porphyry. Quite often the quartz crystals have been slightly re-melted by the surrounding magma. At temperatures below 573° C quartz crystallises as α-quartz, which characteristically forms long prismatic crystals terminated by pyramids (Plate 6). Minerals like quartz which crystallise in slightly different crystal forms within given temperature ranges, are known as *geological thermometers*. There are also minerals whose form gives some indication of the pressure prevalent during their formation. These are sometimes called *geological manometers*.

In plutonic rocks well-formed minerals developed during the main phase of crystallisation are very rare. Usually, adjoining simultaneously formed crystals have interfered with each others'

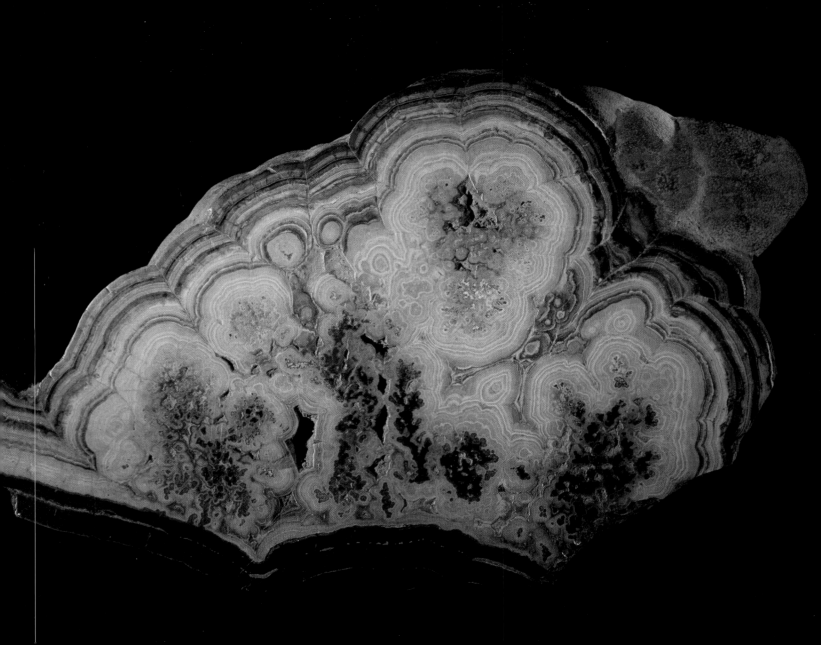

39 CHRYSOPRASE (Green Chalcedony). Pale leek-green unevenly coloured specimen with conchoidal fracture surfaces, the colour due to admixture of small quantities of nickel ▪ From Kosemütz, Silesia ▪ Name from Greek *chrysos*—gold—and *prason*—leek ▪ SiO_2, cryptocrystalline ▪ Scale 2·3:1

growth. In contrast to this, it is common to find phenocrysts in extrusive rocks which have a perfectly developed crystal shape. As long as the rock is fresh it is difficult to extract the phenocrysts of augite, hornblende, feldspar or feldspathoids from it. But if the rock is somewhat weathered it is often quite simple to get idiomorphic crystals out of the ground-mass without damaging them. Among the rock types yielding such phenocrysts are the volcanic tuffs; these may contain large euhedral hornblendes, augites or biotites. Well-formed crystals of this type are so common in some loosely consolidated tuffs that these have been termed crystal tuffs.

2. Minerals in Druses and Veins in Volcanic Rocks

Magma brought to the surface by active volcanoes emits enormous amounts of steam. In addition to superheated water, magma contains in solution large quantities of carbon dioxide, sulphur dioxide and compounds of chlorine, fluorine and boron; these gases escape to the atmosphere when the pressure on the magma is reduced. They also form small bubbles or vesicles in the lava, which may remain as such if the lava is already very viscous. Chemical reaction between the volcanic gases on the one hand and the hot magma and newly crystallised minerals on the other may produce yet other minerals, which are often well crystallised. The places where hot gases and vapours are given off by active volcanoes are termed *fumaroles*, and the sites emitting rather cooler vapours from nearly extinct or quiescent volcanoes are called *solfataras*. In areas of virtually extinct volcanic activity one often finds thermal springs and small vents where carbon dioxide is emitted. Apart from sulphur and sassoline, which is native boric acid, several dozen minerals can, according to the

84

40 TETRAHEDRITE (Fahlerz or Grey Copper). Steel-grey tetrahedral crystals associated with colourless translucent quartz and, top right, with a brownish film of limonite ▪ From Kapnik, Transylvania, Rumania ▪ Name from Greek *tetrahednos*—four-sided—because of its tetrahedral habit ▪ $(Cu_2, Ag_2, Fe, ZN)_3Sb_2S_6$, cubic ▪ Quartz, SiO_2, hexagonal ▪ Limonite, $FeOOH + nH_2O$, amorphous ▪ Scale 2·1 : 1

temperature and chemical composition of the escaping gases, be formed on the sides of fumaroles and solfataras. Particularly interesting mineral assemblages containing rare minerals are formed in areas where volcanic gases are emitted under the sea, or where they set up chemical reactions with carbonates present in the adjoining rocks. All minerals so formed are as a rule perfectly crystallised, though usually fairly small.

The druses of basalts, andesites and other volcanic rocks frequently contain *zeolite*. The numerous members of this prolific mineral family usually occur in the form of white or colourless crystals or as brownish aggregates. According to their habit, one can recognise granular, platy or fibrous zeolites. A widely distributed mineral belonging to this group is natrolite, a fibrous zeolite which can be found in a great variety of forms in veins and druses (Plate 19). A very small admixture of limonite gives these minerals a yellowish or ochre-brown colour. The vesicles and cavities in volcanic rocks which are filled with such late-formed minerals are called *amygdales*. Some druses are completely filled with *chalcedony;* others are lined with a thin layer of it, from which crystals of quartz or amethyst project into the cavity. A mineral which is commonly associated with chalcedony in druses is calcite. Specular haematite, ruby-mica and haematite often form films or incrustations over the projecting crystals. Cavities of irregular shape are called *lithophyses*. These occur in rhyolites, quartz porphyries and other acid extrusive rocks, and are most commonly filled with chalcedony, agate, tridymite, quartz, haematite or carbonates. Chalcedony is a *cryptocrystalline* form of silica. The term cryptocrystalline denotes a mineral aggregate composed of minute crystallites which can be recognised as such only with the aid of a microscope. In contrast to this, the term *phanerocrystalline* describes an aggregate in which the individual

41 RHODOCHROSITE (Dialogite). Bands of various shades of red around massive brownish-black psilomelane ■ From Restauradora, Capillatas County, Catamarca Province, Argentine ■ $MnCO_3$, hexagonal ■ Psilomelane, predominantly hydrated MnO_2, monoclinic ■ Scale 2·5 : 1

crystals can be plainly distinguished with the naked eye. Chalcedony, therefore, is an aggregate of minute quartz fibres, which in some varieties of the mineral are enclosed in an amorphous groundmass of opal. It usually forms irregular masses which as a rule are reniform or botryoidal in shape, but can also be nodular, stalactitic or encrusting. The colour of chalcedony ranges from pale and translucent to black and opaque, and it can possess several colours which are often arranged in a concentric pattern (Plates 20, 21). The more characteristic colour varieties of chalcedony form well-known gemstones which have been given separate names. *Agate*, for instance, consists of concentric layers of variously coloured chalcedony (Plate 22). There are other forms of agate, such as onyx, which has black and white bands, and moss- or tree-agate, which is a milky variety with dendritic (tree-shaped) inclusions.

Some basalts and related basic volcanic rocks have amygdales or druses containing *amethyst* (Plate 2). The crystals of amethyst usually project from a basal layer of chalcedony whose colour differs from that of the amethyst. In some localities the colour of the amethyst is variable, ranging from pale to deep violet with a bluish or reddish tint. The druses, which may weigh up to a hundredweight, contain amethyst crystals whose tips only are of gemstone quality. The parts of the crystals nearer the walls are usually cloudy and useless as gemstones.

The extraction of agates from fresh volcanic rocks is both laborious and tricky, as the druses can easily be damaged. The most profitable areas for collecting are therefore the areas where the rock is weathered to such an extent that the agates can be easily loosened, or, better still, where they have been washed out by streams or rivers and deposited in loose river gravels.

Thermal springs often deposit a siliceous sinter known as *geyserite*. This is a solidified gel composed

42 BARYTES (Heavy Spar). Near-spherical masses of cockscomb-like aggregates of lamellar crystals in association with large distorted cubes of fluorspar, small crystals of quartz and general incrustations of red-brown limonite ▪ From Wieden, Black Forest, Germany ▪ $BaSo_4$, orthorhombic ▪ Fluorspar, CaF_2, cubic ▪ Limonite, $FeOOH + nH_2O$, amorphous ▪ Scale 1·5:1

of hydrated silica and is a form of *opal*. It is often found as a porous deposit round hot springs and in amygdales in recent basalts, andesites and trachytes, as well as in joints and veins in other recent volcanic rocks.

The glassy transparent variety of opal is known as hyalite. Precious opal—that is, the variety of opal which is regarded as a gemstone—is opalescent with a brilliant, fiery play of colours. Stones of particular value are those with a bluish or greenish sheen. Fire-opal has a fiery red or brownish-red sheen. When opal forms the ground-mass of the adjacent country rock, the rock itself is known as opal matrix, which is also used as a gemstone.

The 'opalescence' of opal is not a permanent feature, as the mineral tends to lose its combined water when kept in a dry atmosphere and in consequence loses its attractive play of colour. One way of preventing this process of desiccation is to put the stone from time to time into water, or to keep it in a raw potato.

3. Pegmatitic and Pneumatolitic Minerals

A large but variable number of minerals is formed after the main phase of the crystallisation of the magma is completed. During the crystallisation of a plutonic rock the residual magma becomes progressively richer in water and other volatile substances. This superheated aqueous solution contains a number of volatile compounds whose constituent elements could not readily be incorporated in the minerals already crystallised. The most important of these are lithium, beryllium, zirconium, boron, fluorine, niobium, tantalium, thorium, uranium and the rare earth elements.

The pressure in these superheated solutions is very great, and is constantly being increased by the addition of further liquid from the cooling magma.

These hot residual solutions will deposit their minerals only if the rocks above the magma chamber can effectively prevent their rapid escape. In the case of extrusive rocks, for instance, there is nothing to prevent the escape of gases and vapours, and pegmatitic minerals are never formed. At temperatures ranging from 700° down to 550° C large crystals of silicate minerals start to crystallise. The coarse-grained rocks formed at this stage are termed *pegmatites*, and these form clearly defined veins or masses near the roofs or side-walls of plutonic intrusions. Most pegmatites are associated with granites and similar acid plutonic rocks. Much more rarely they are found in syenites and nepheline syenites, and hardly ever in basic plutonic rocks.

Most pegmatites are coarsely crystalline aggregates of quartz and feldspar, which may also contain muscovite and tourmaline. Quite frequently pegmatites contain rare minerals, and some are made up almost entirely of rare and valuable minerals.

It is not usually possible to establish a regular sequence of crystallisation of the pegmatite minerals, which may often have crystallised more or less simultaneously. There are, for example, peculiar intergrowths of quartz and orthoclase or microcline, which in section have the shape of Runic or Semitic hieroglyphics and are known as graphic intergrowths. Some pegmatite masses are roughly zoned, with the central core containing different minerals and larger crystals than the outer zones. In the marginal areas of granite masses which have been soaked by pegmatitic solutions one sometimes finds small irregular cavities lined with pegmatites. These cavities are called *miaro-lites*, the term having been originally coined for them by Italian stone-masons. The miarolites

often contain rosettes of muscovite, perfect small crystals of quartz and plates of haematite. The larger druses in the pegmatitic zones of granites may yield perfect crystals of a variety of minerals. The crystals of coarse pegmatites projecting into the empty cavities of druses often have completely clear or finely coloured ends, which can be cut and polished as gemstones. Pegmatites are thus important sources not only of minerals which provide raw materials for industry, but also of gemstones. Emerald, one of the most valuable gemstones, may form in pegmatite under the following circumstances: if a pegmatitic solution containing beryllium crystallises within a rock containing traces of chrome, the newly formed pegmatite will contain dark green transparent emerald (Plate 25) instead of the more usual cloudy white to greyish-green beryl.

The pegmatite minerals which crystallise from hot aqueous solutions are formed in an environment particularly suitable for the perfect growth of crystals. The solutions are very mobile and contain only a small number of crystal nuclei, so that there is less chance of mutual interference during crystal growth. The minerals of pegmatites are thus not only of good crystalline shape but reach a surprising size. The largest crystals found in the earth's crust are, in fact, from pegmatites. Gigantic crystals of alkali-feldspar, muscovite, phlogopite, spodumene and beryl are known, and some crystals of spodumene and beryl from pegmatites weigh nearly 100 tons.

Pegmatites, besides being the source of very large crystals, also provide perfect crystals of common minerals as well as of very rare minerals. Some contain minerals of the elements scandium and yttrium, as well as cerium and other rare earths. We know of pegmatites with virtually unique mineral assemblages, while some mineral species are found only among pegmatite minerals. One of the few pegmatite minerals which never form well-shaped crystals is rose quartz.

As the temperature of the residual fluid in the crystallising magma sinks still further, the proportion of volatile constituents goes on increasing, till the liquid is very rich in water and gases. The late magmatic minerals crystallising from such solutions at temperatures between 550° and about 400° C are termed *pneumatolites*. Whereas in granite pegmatites the most common minerals are quartz, potassium feldspar and muscovite, in pneumatolitic mineral assemblage these silicates are relatively unimportant. The characteristic silicate minerals here are topaz, lithium mica and tourmaline (Plate 26), which is the most widespread boron mineral. Other typically pneumatolitic minerals are cassiterite, wolframite, scheelite (Plate 27) and molybdenite (Plate 28).

The chemically active pneumatolitic solutions can penetrate very readily into limestones and other carbonate-rich country rocks and react with these to form new minerals. In this fashion mineral assemblages with large numbers of minerals are formed, and many localities where they have been found are now world-famous for the variety and perfect form of their minerals. Calcium, magnesium and iron silicates, as well as valuable ore minerals, are characteristic of these mineral assemblages. Compact masses of calciumsilicate minerals which are closely inter-grown are known as *skarn*, a term first used by Swedish ore-miners.

The residual pneumatolitic solutions frequently crystallise out in veins; that is, they fill up joints and cracks in the rock through which they have passed. The solutions can also react chemically both with the granitic rocks from whose magma they were derived and with the older rocks surrounding the granite. As a result of these reactions, new minerals such as tourmaline and topaz are formed in the adjoining granite, and in extreme cases parts of the granite may be converted

into rock consisting almost entirely of these minerals. Rocks in which cassiterite has been formed by this reaction are known by the old German mining term *greisen*.

There are many mineral assemblages which are transitional between the true pegmatitic and pneumatolitic types, and these are sometimes called *pegmatitic-pneumatolitic*. A typical assemblage of this kind was found in the tin mines in the Erzgebirge (Ore Mountains) along the border between Bohemia and Saxony, where cassiterite is usually associated with scheelite (Plate 27), wolframite, arsenopyrite, zinnwaldite and tourmaline (Plate 26).

4. Minerals of Hydrothermal Origin

When the temperature of the residual magmatic fluid falls still further, it eventually passes a critical temperature below which it becomes a watery liquid constituting a true solution. Above the critical temperature the mineral solutions are in a superheated gaseous or fluid condition. The critical temperature of the steam of pure water is 374° C at a pressure of 225 atmospheres, but in the case of the residual solution of a natural magma this temperature is lower and varies somewhat according to the type and the amount of dissolved substances. At this critical temperature the *hydrothermal minerals* crystallise from the thin residual liquid. The solutions penetrate through fissures in the rock, and in these the crystallising minerals form thin veinlets or thick mineral veins, according to the space available. The solutions can also permeate porous rocks which become impregnated with minerals, and they can dissolve and replace readily soluble rocks, such as lime-stones. In this manner impregnation and replacement lodes are formed.

47 PYROLUSITE. Dark dendrites weathered out from flaggy sandstone ▪ From Ebersbach, near Aschaffenburg, Spessart, Germany ▪ Name from Greek *pyr*—fire—and *lusios*—destroying—because it was used to remove the green colour from molten glass ▪ MnO_2, tetragonal ▪ Scale 1·8:1

Hydrothermal mineralising solutions may be derived from the magmas of extrusive and hypabyssal rocks, as well as from plutonic magmas. Most hydrothermal minerals occur in ore or mineral veins. The fissures and faults in which these minerals were deposited were usually formed during earth movements, and it is thus most usual to find ore veins in areas where the crust has undergone some tectonic disturbance. Quite often the country rock on either side of a mineral vein is bleached, hydrothermally altered, silicified or riddled with minute veinlets of ore minerals branching out from the main vein. Thin beds of clay composed of ground-up rock may occur along the wall of a vein which traverses sheared or fractured rock.

Ore or mineral veins may be either solitary or they may occur in swarms. An area where mineral veins are common is called a mineralised zone. Often the veins in a mineralised zone containing the same group of minerals have a more or less uniform trend, indicating that they utilised a system of joints which were opened by a system of crustal stresses operating at that time.

The direction of a steeply dipping ore vein cropping out on a horizontal surface is usually called the *strike* of the vein.

The thickness of a vein and the depth to which economically important minerals within the vein may extend are factors of importance to the ore-miner. There are some hydrothermal ore veins whose mineral content remains uniform to a great depth. Other mineral veins have a horizontally layered structure, so that different minerals and ore associations are found at different depths. The mineral content of a vein can also vary horizontally in the direction of strike. If a large number of distinctive mineral assemblages of no great vertical extent follow one another in a downward

direction, the vein is said to be *telescoped*. Veins of this type are often rich in well-crystallised minerals, particularly if there are drusy patches in the vein.

Hydrothermal solutions, however, do not deposit their mineral content only in veins. The pore spaces and cavities of conglomerates, sandstones, tuffs and vesicular volcanic rocks may all be filled with hydrothermal minerals. In sedimentary rocks whose pore spaces are thus impregnated, large crystals cannot develop. Some sedimentary rocks, such as limestones and other carbonate rocks, which can react chemically with hydrothermal solutions, may be partially replaced by new groups of minerals. Such mineral lodes are called metasomatic or replacement deposits. Hydrothermal mineral veins occur not only in fissures within the parent igneous body and its immediate vicinity, but, since watery solutions can travel for considerable distances both upwards and laterally, they may also be found in veins, replacement deposits or impregnations in quite unrelated rocks, in whose vicinity there may be no sign of igneous rock. Many hydrothermal ore provinces which are not near any large igneous body have been assumed, and sometimes proved, to be above a granitic pluton emplaced at depth.

In the case of hydrothermal mineral assemblages, it is usually possible to ascertain a definite order of formation, since the crystallisation of vein minerals follows definite physical and chemical laws. The order of crystallisation in ore veins is known as the *succession*. The minerals in some hydro-thermal veins may have crystallised during a number of distinct phases, whenever solution became available, and usually the order of crystallisation in each such phase was the same. The minerals quartz, sulphide ores, barytes and carbonate may sometimes be seen to have crystallised two or more times in that order in one mineral vein. Not infrequently one finds that minerals which

49 WAVELLITE. Spherical nodular aggregates with radiating structure, in blue-grey flinty slate ▪ From Langenstriegis, Saxony, Germany ▪ Named after its discoverer Wavell ▪ $Al_3[(OH)_3/(PO_4)_2]\cdot 5H_2O$, orthorhombic ▪ Scale 3·8:1

crystallised at an early stage were dissolved again during a later stage. The shapes, or ghosts, of such vanished crystals may remain as cavities in minerals formed later.

More than a hundred distinct minerals are known to occur in mineral and ore veins. The compounds of sulphur, arsenic, antimony and bismuth give rise to a particularly large number of ore minerals. The non-metallic minerals—usually of no commercial value—associated with ore minerals in hydrothermal veins are called *gangue* by the ore-miners. The most common gangue minerals are quartz, calcite and other carbonates, fluorspar and barytes.

The unusual feature of hydrothermal mineral assemblages is the large number of different minerals that are often present within a very small space. It is by no means uncommon to find half-a-dozen different minerals in one vein. The variety of forms of individual minerals is also surprising. For instance, the same mineral may occur in a number of generations in one vein, in each case with a different crystal habit, colour and size. The metallic lustre of the ore minerals—sulphides, arsenides and oxides—usually contrasts strikingly with that of the gangue minerals, which are quite differently coloured and usually translucent or transparent. The mineral association, together with the habit and colour of the minerals and the number of generations of minerals present, is often very distinctive, and the expert can frequently recognize the actual vein by examining a small specimen and may even be able to tell in which area within a mine the particular mineral assemblage occurs. Many minerals found in hydrothermal veins and deposits are of commercial value, and they have long been intensely studied as they are the most important sources of the ores of gold, silver, lead, zinc, bismuth, uranium, antimony, mercury and other important metals. The small areas in which there is a concentration of ore minerals are called *ore shoots*. Such concentrations are often

104

50 CHALCOPYRITE. Massive brass-yellow ore, in places largely altered to dark bornite (bottom left), and a mixture of various secondary copper minerals; white quartz veined with green malachite; thin crust of limonite near top ▪ From Wildschapbachtal, Black Forest, Germany ▪ Name chalcopyrite from Greek *chalcos*— copper—and *pyr*—fire ▪ $CuFeS_2$, tetragonal ▪ Malachite, $CU_2[(OH)_2/CO_3]$, monoclinic ▪ Bornite, Cu_5FeS_4, cubic ▪ Scale 1·7:1

51 CHALCOPYRITE. Brass-yellow crystals with metallic lustre and characteristic bands of twinning, associated with pale crystals of calcite and brownish crystals of ankerite ▪ From St Andreasberg, Harz Mountains, Germany ▪ $CuFeS_2$, tetragonal ▪ Calcite, $CaCO_3$, hexagonal ▪ Ankerite, $(Mg, Fe, Mn)CO_3$, hexagonal ▪ Scale 3·1:1

found in places where several ore veins come together or cross each other. If the proportion of ore minerals to gangue within the seam decreases, the vein is said to become impoverished.

If the fissure containing a mineral vein is wide open, the individual minerals can during growth develop their own crystal form without hindrance. This is particularly the case if the actual widening of the fissure was more rapid than the filling-up with mineral substance. Under such favourable conditions, a very large number of diverse crystal shapes may be developed. In these cases the actual shape of the growing crystal not only depends on the atomic structure of the particular mineral, but is also influenced by environmental conditions. Particularly fine crystals are found among the minerals that crystallised last, as these were able to grow in the open space without any extraneous interference.

Many beautiful crystal groups have been obtained from mines working hydrothermal veins. Because of these specimens the names of many old mines, in both Europe and the New World, which have long since been worked out, are still remembered today. A large number of fine mineral specimens to be found in museums all over the world came from old mines in the Black Forest, Harz Mountains and Erzgebirge, and from mines in Derbyshire and Cornwall. The account books of some of these old mines show that one to two centuries ago they had a considerable income not only from the ores but from the fine mineral specimens which they sold to museums and private collectors.

In contrast to the metallic, lustrous and opaque ore minerals, most gangue minerals are pale, predominantly white, yellowish, brownish or greenish, and partially or completely transparent or

52 CHRYSOCOLLA. Minute green botryoidal aggregates resulting from the weathering of copper ore ▪ From Lipari Islands, Italy ▪ Name from Greek *chrysos*—gold—and *kolla*—glue—because the mineral was used as a soldering flux for gold ▪ $CuSiO_3 \cdot nH_2O$, cryptocrystalline, possibly orthorhombic ▪ Scale 4·3:1

translucent. Many gangue minerals are easily split along their cleavage faces and were thus often called *spat* by the old German miners. The form -spat or -spar is now a common suffix of many mineral names.

Some minerals in hydrothermal assemblages have the shape of other, sometimes unrelated, minerals. These are called *pseudomorphs*, and they were formed when a pre-existing mineral was gradually dissolved out and the space so formed simultaneously filled by a new mineral. The original crystal shape is thus preserved. The presence of pseudomorphs in a mineral assemblage provides important clues as to the sequence of crystallisation in rocks and mineral deposits, because their shape gives an indication of types of minerals which were originally present.

If hydrothermal solutions are able to crystallise in an open fissure, the minerals of succeeding generations will form a succession of layers, with the oldest on the side adjoining the rock. Symmetrically layered mineral and ore veins are formed in this fashion. If during the process of crystallisation the country rock is involved in earth movements and is shattered, the angular fragments of rock become encrusted with ore and gangue-minerals, and mineralised breccia (Plate 29) is formed. The individual rock fragments are coated with ores and are set in a matrix of gangue minerals.

As has already been mentioned, ore minerals crystallise from solutions in a definite order as the temperature falls. Hydrothermal deposits and ore formations can therefore be classified according to their ore and mineral content, and mineral lodes are usually named according to their characteristic minerals. Ore veins containing argentiferous galena and other silver ores in a gangue of

53 · CHALCANTHITE (Blue Vitriol). Group of blue triclinic tabular crystals with thin needles of melanterite (green vitriol) ▪ From Coquimbo, Chile ▪ Name from Greek *chalkos*—copper—and *anthos*—bloom—because of the efflorescence on many copper ores ▪ $Cu[SO_4] \cdot 5H_2O$, triclinic ▪ Name melanterite from Greek *melanteria*— earthy tenorite ▪ $Fe[SO_4] \cdot 7H_2O$, monoclinic ▪ Scale 3·2:1

fluorspar and barytes are classed as the fluor-barytes lead-silver formation. In such ore formations one always finds minerals composed of a definite set of elements.

The veins or *reefs* of the gold-silver formation contain native gold, either intergrown with coarse quartz gangue or as foil-, thread- or grain-like aggregates of very variable size and shape (Plates 10, 30, 34). The largest known single piece of gold, weighing 40 kilograms, was found in a gold-quartz vein in California. Some gold veins contain an alloy of gold and silver known as argentiferous gold or electrum, as well as such rare gold minerals as gold tellurides and selenides, together with silver ores. Gold-silver ores associated with volcanic complexes are famous for the beautiful crystal forms found in druses within the veins.

Quartz veins containing native gold generally contain some iron ore too, usually brownish or yellowish limonite. At greater depths these veins contain auriferous pyrite. Next to the gold-bearing sediments, such veins are the most important sources of this precious metal.

To the copper sulphide formation belong the important deposits containing massive *pyrite* and *chalcopyrite*. The lens- or stock-shaped ore bodies of these minerals may reach tremendous proportions, but they rarely contain well-developed crystals. Other copper sulphide deposits occur as impregnations which may yield large quantities of the ores of copper and other metals, but no large crystals. The only deposits of this group of ores to contain well-formed crystals are those found in veins or druses associated with volcanic rocks. Native copper is found in cavities in ancient extrusive rocks, where it may form massive bodies several tons in weight. In these rocks it may also occur in branching arborescent aggregates of distorted crystals (Plate 31), or in thin sheets or plates.

110

54 MALACHITE. Fibrous sheafs of long prismatic crystals associated with reddish cuprite of earthy texture and crystals of yellowish calcite ▪ From Gumechevsk, Ural Mountains, U.S.S.R. ▪ $Cu_2[(OH_2)/CO_3]$, monoclinic ▪ Cuprite, Cu_2O, cubic ▪ Calcite, $CaCO_3$, hexagonal ▪ Scale 3·1:1

An important member of this group of ores and the most important copper ore is chalcopyrite, which usually forms massive aggregates (Plate 50). Much more rarely it forms well-developed brass-yellow twinned crystals with distorted faces (Plate 51).

Most of the earth's hydrothermal ore veins belong to the lead–silver–zinc mineral association. The most important minerals found in these deposits are argentiferous galena, zinc blende, pyrite, tetrahedrite, chalcopyrite, bornite, and silver ores. Many ore veins of this type have provided fine specimens of these minerals. Druses containing perfect crystals of galena (Plates 4, 33) and blende (Plate 35) are in some areas just as common as well-developed crystals of the gangue minerals, such as calcite (Plates 12, 13).

When *galena* contains a small quantity of silver, it is a valuable silver ore. Its usual crystal form is the cube, but it may also occur as a combination with many faces, and may produce crystals of considerable size. More rarely it forms skeletal, massive, nodular or granular aggregates. The variety which has been squeezed out and distorted by earth movements is called foliated galena. Galena is lead-grey in colour, like metallic lead, and its freshly exposed cleavage faces have a bright metallic lustre. The outer surface of galena crystals, however, is usually tarnished and dull.

Blende or *sphalerite*, the sulphide of zinc, in which part of the zinc is usually replaced by iron, cadmium and manganese, crystallises in the cubic system and forms distorted crystals with many faces. Blende may also form twinned crystals or may occur in massive form or in irregular grains. Its crystals have adamantine lustre and are opaque and usually dark brown to black. They can also be yellowish, reddish or brown and somewhat translucent. The rhombohedral cleavage faces usually have a gleaming adamantine lustre. The yellow and pale-brown translucent varieties

55 MALACHITE. Green prismatic crystal with smaller tabular crystals of dark-blue azurite ▪ From Tsumeb mine, South-West Africa ▪ $Cu_2[(OH)_2/CO_3]$, monoclinic ▪ Name azurite from French *azur*—sky-blue ▪ $Cu_3[(OH)_2/CO_3)_2]$, monoclinic ▪ Scale 6·4:1

of blende are sometimes called honey-blende, and the red variety is ruby-blende. Botryoidal, fibrous or massive aggregates of blende with a concentrically banded internal structure are fairly common. These forms often contain an admixture of wurtzite, another form of zinc sulphide, as well as galena (Plate 38).

A common mineral in the lead-silver ore assemblage, as well as among other hydrothermal ores, is *tetrahedrite*, also known as *fahlerz*. This mineral may form either massive aggregates or very well-developed tetrahedral crystals with striated faces. The name tetrahedrite is used for a family of closely related minerals whose members contain copper and silver, and sometimes zinc, iron or mercury, as well as sulphur, antimony, arsenic or bismuth (Plate 40).

Another common mineral assemblage in hydrothermal veins is that containing the elements *silver, cobalt, nickel, bismuth* and *uranium*. Such veins are remarkable for their large number of associated mineral species and it is not uncommon to find two dozen or more distinct minerals in a single vein. Examples of well-crystallised minerals in deposits of this type are native silver (Plate 36), red silver ore (ruby silver) (Plate 37), and gangue minerals of the carbonate group (Plate 8). Tree-shaped aggregates of native silver are often made up of small cubes and octahedra (Plate 36). The large crystals of translucent ruby silver, often occurring in very fine crystal groups (Plate 37), are also important silver ores. The gleaming adamantine lustre of most specimens of ruby silver is lost on exposure to sunlight, and the crystals tend to become coated with a grey film of silver. The specimens of ruby silver in museums and other mineral collections are therefore best kept away from strong sunlight.

114

56 PHOSPHOCHALCITE. Coarse milky quartz with nodular incrustations and in the cavity a felted mass of fine dark green crystals ▪ From Virneberg, near Rheinbreitbach, Siebengebirge, Germany ▪ Name from Greek *phosphoros*—light-bearer—and *chalkos*—copper—because of its constituents ▪ $Cu_5[(OH)_2/PO_4]_2$, monoclinic ▪ Scale 2:1

Aqueous solutions whose temperature is below the boiling point of water are responsible for the formation of veins containing the ores of *antimony* and *mercury*. Such veins are relatively rare and rather poorer in mineral species than the mineral assemblages described above. The most important antimony mineral in these veins, and also the most important mineral ore, is stibnite. This can occur in a great variety of forms, but its crystals are most commonly thin, pointed needles, with a metallic lustre which tarnishes readily (Plate 63). The most important mercury ore in this assemblage is cinnabar.

Mineral veins containing oxides of *iron*, *manganese* and *magnesia* are very widespread. These minerals crystallised from hydrothermal solutions at a relatively low temperature, and usually contain only few mineral species. The most important are siderite, haematite, manganese-bearing minerals of the pyrolusite group, rhodochrosite and magnesite. Whereas the most important minerals of the ore groups described so far are the sulphides, in this group the oxides, hydroxides and carbonates predominate. Siderite forms large stock-like masses both in ore veins and in replacement deposits. Magnesite, too, forms sizeable replacement deposits in limestones and dolomites. In iron-manganese ore veins one may find fine crystal groups of rose-red rhodochrosite (Plates 5, 43).

Finally, there are hydrothermal veins completely devoid of ore minerals. These are made up entirely of gangue minerals, such as quartz, fluorspar, barytes and calcite. Druses and cavities in such veins often yield perfect crystals of barytes and fluorspar. The barytes in the druses appears in a great variety of forms, including platy or prismatic crystals with wedge-shaped sides; flat

116

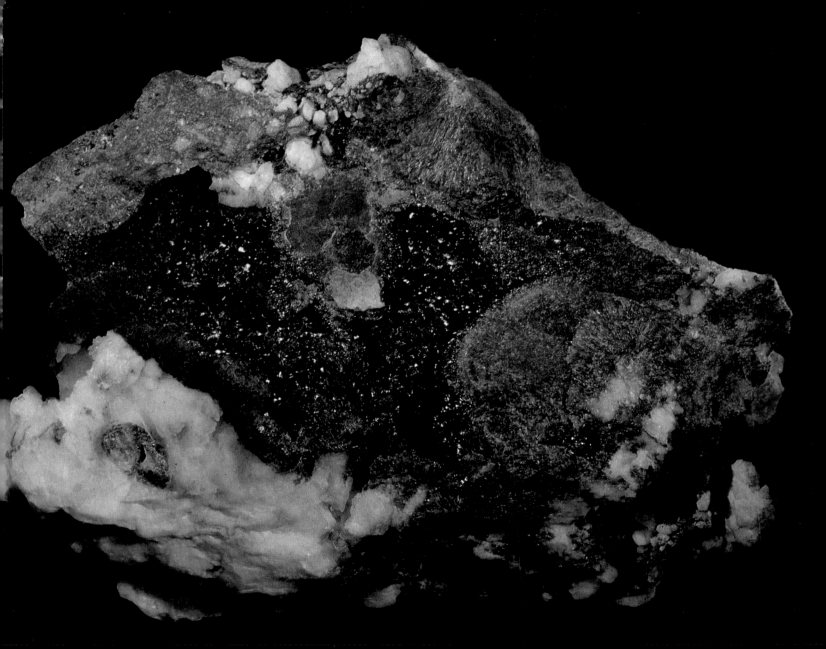

57 TORBERNITE (Copper Uranite). Thin green platy crystals in foliaceous aggregates ▪ From Vernon, Cornwall, England ▪ Named after the Swedish chemist Torbern Bergman ▪ $Cu[UO_2/PO_4]_2 \cdot 10H_2O$, tetragonal ▪ Scale 2·7:1

plates or thin lamellar crystals which may be arranged in rosettes, cockscomb or fan-shaped groups; scaly aggregates, or compact masses (Plates 7, 42). Fluorspar, whose lustre resembles that of damp glass, most commonly crystallises as cubes, or, more rarely, forms combinations with many faces. It may be colourless and completely clear, or may appear in a large variety of colours.

Apart from calcite, which produces a great variety of crystal forms and many shades of colour, there are numerous other carbonates in these veins. Dolomite and siderite, as well as ankerite, are very common.

Quartz is present in the hydrothermal veins of all ore groups. It is found not only in association with other gangue minerals, but often forms veins composed entirely of quartz. Often the deeper portions of hydrothermal veins containing a variety of minerals are made up exclusively of quartz. Quartz, like other gangue minerals, occurs in many different forms. In compact veins it is coarsely crystalline and devoid of druses. Though usually clear, it may appear cloudy or milky if it contains minute inclusions of liquid, in which case it is called milky quartz. Quite often vein quartz is dense and compact like flint, and displays colour-banding like chalcedony. It may replace other gangue minerals, and when it projects into cavities it forms nearly perfect crystals.

5. Minerals of Sedimentary Origin

The weathering of extrusive igneous rocks starts immediately after they are formed. Hypabyssal and plutonic rocks as well as metamorphic rocks appear on the surface only when the overlying rocks are eroded away, but all may eventually be exposed to the forces of denudation. The climatic

118

58 PYROMORPHITE (Green Lead Ore). Grass-green prismatic and pointed crystals lining a cavity in limonite ▪ From Hofsgrund am Schauinsland, Black Forest, Germany ▪ Name from Greek *pyr*—fire—and *morphe*—shape—because it changes shape and forms a globule of lead in the flame of a blowpipe ▪ $Pb_5[Cl/(PO_4)_3]$, hexagonal ▪ Scale 1·9:1

and physical conditions determine whether the mechanical disintegration and chemical weathering of the minerals of these rocks is slow or rapid. Eventually the rock debris and the material in solution are re-deposited, forming in the course of time new minerals and rocks. The materials deposited in lakes and rivers, in the sea and in deserts, are called sediments, and the rocks formed by their compaction are sedimentary rocks.

The jointing and exfoliation caused by frost action facilitates the weathering of rocks in mountainous areas, and the lower slopes of mountains are often littered with large blocks and masses of scree made up of fragments of various sizes. The scree may be carried away and further broken up by streams, rivers, ice and ocean currents, and eventually re-deposited to form *clastic* sediments. The shape and size of the mineral grains in clastic sediments tell us something of the way in which the individual particles were transported and deposited. In a water-borne deposit the small sand grains are usually angular, the larger pebbles and blocks well rounded. Wind-deposited sand grains, on the other hand, are usually very well rounded, hence the name millet seed grains often applied to them. The blocks and pebbles of an ice-borne deposit, such as boulder clay, have rounded-off corners and smooth faces with parallel scratches. Sediments of this kind are highly assorted, with large boulders often embedded in fine clay.

Sedimentary rock formed by the consolidation of gravel is called *conglomerate* or, if the individual pebbles are highly angular, *breccia*. The best known of the finer-grained clastic sediments are, in order of decreasing grain size, sandstone, siltstone and shale.

We can get some idea of the environment in which a sedimentary rock was deposited by studying the fossils, sedimentary structures and minerals in the rock. Sediments deposited in the sea are

120

59 WULFENITE. Aggregate of honey-yellow resinous tabular crystals on decomposed galena ▪ From Bleiberg, near Villach, Carinthia, Austria ▪ Named after the Austrian mineralogist Wulfen ▪ Pb[MoO$_4$], tetragonal ▪ Scale 3:1

called *marine*; fresh-water lake deposits, *limnic*; river and stream deposits, *fluviatile*; deposits laid down by land ice, *glacial*; and those carried by glacial melt-waters, *fluvio-glacial*. Sediments laid down on dry land are called *terrestrial*, and those transported and deposited by wind, *aeolian*.

Many diverse factors enter into the formation of sediments. The character of the original detritus, the means by which and how far it was carried, the environment of deposition and the prevailing climatic conditions all play a part in determining the type of sediment formed. The consolidation of an uncompacted sediment may in the course of time be accomplished either by compression due to the weight of overlying sediment, or by the deposition of lime, silica or some other cementing material in the pore spaces. The chemical change which takes place in sediments shortly after their deposition is called *diagenesis*. The hardness of a sediment is not, of course, in any way a measure of its age. Some very ancient clays, for instance, are still plastic, whereas many recent scree deposits have been naturally cemented to form iron-hard breccias.

When they are exposed to the forces of denudation on the earth's surface, the minerals of igneous and metamorphic rocks, which were formed under very different conditions of temperature and pressure, are to a varying extent decomposed and dissolved. This is particularly true in the case of feldspars, which decompose readily into clay minerals. Quartz, on the other hand, is chemically stable and insoluble under atmospheric conditions: and as it is hard and has no cleavage, it is not readily broken up or ground down. For this reason quartz is the most abundant mineral on the earth's surface and is the most important component of many clastic sedimentary rocks. It

60 TURQUOISE. Bluish waxy reniform aggregate of minute triclinic crystals ▪ From Nischapur (Chorassan Province), Persia ▪ Name derived from the Chaldean name for this mineral, *torkeja*, as it came to Europe via Turkey ▪ $CuAl_6[(OH)_8/(PO_4)_4] \cdot 4H_2O$, triclinic ▪ Scale 1·3:1

forms the greater part of most sandstones and unconsolidated sand deposits. During the weathering of the dark mica *biotite*, iron is first of all dissolved out and the mineral takes on a golden lustre. As its decomposition proceeds, it loses magnesium and becomes pale and silvery. The weathering of iron-rich minerals produces hydroxide of iron, which is re-deposited in sediments as limonite and imparts to them a brownish or reddish colour. Sediments containing a high proportion of limonite may be important iron ores. Hydrated iron oxide can also be deposited as a crystalline variety of limonite known as needle iron ore. In many iron-bearing sedimentary rocks minerals are dissolved out to produce ground water charged with dissolved oxides and hydroxides of iron, manganese and aluminium. These are re-deposited not only as limonite but also as various iron and manganese minerals. The dendrites (Plates 46, 47) frequently seen along joints and bedding planes are formed in this way.

Among the most important minerals of clastic sedimentary rocks are the *clay minerals*. These minute, scaly mineral particles are produced by the weathering of feldspars and other aluminium silicates. The clay minerals are incapable of forming even small crystals, and individual clay particles can only be seen with the maximum microscopic magnification.

Calcite, which in the form of limestone forms a high proportion of many sedimentary rock formations, is the most abundant carbonate mineral. The second in importance is *dolomite*, which together with calcite forms many thick beds of dolomitic limestone. Quite frequently organisms, both animal and plant, are largely responsible for the formation of limestones and dolomites, as well as of phosphate and silica rocks. Important sediments formed largely from the remains of plants are peat, lignite, coal and anthracite.

A typical feature of most sedimentary rocks is their *bedding* or *stratification*; this is particularly well developed when the sediment is formed of particles of varying size which were deposited under quiet conditions. The separate layers, or strata, of an undisturbed sedimentary rock are bounded by horizontal planes called bedding planes. The thickness of individual beds depends on the conditions of the sediment's deposition. Very thin beds are known as *laminae* and a group of beds of the same type is called a *set*. Beds are said to be *concordant* if they succeed one another without any break or angular disconformity. If a period of non-deposition or erosion, possibly with uplift and folding, intervened between the formation of two succeeding beds, the beds are said to be *discordant*, and the surface between them is an *unconformity*. Quite often an unconformity separates old intensely folded sediments from much younger near-horizontal strata.

Apart from strata with essentially parallel bedding, sediments often exhibit *cross-stratification* or *cross-bedding*. This is characteristically developed when sediments were deposited by variable currents in rivers, lakes or near the sea-shore, or by variable winds in deserts.

Deposits of economically important minerals such as coals and iron ores, which form concordant layers in a sedimentary succession, are termed *seams*. As is the case with other sedimentary beds, these seams may thin out laterally.

Many sedimentary rocks contain *fossils*. These remains of animals and plants tell us something of the evolution of life on our planet. In many cases only the hard parts of the organisms remain, and even these have usually been replaced by calcite, silica or other minerals. For instance, the skeletons of fossil fish from the Kupferschiefer, a copper-bearing shale in Germany, have been replaced by

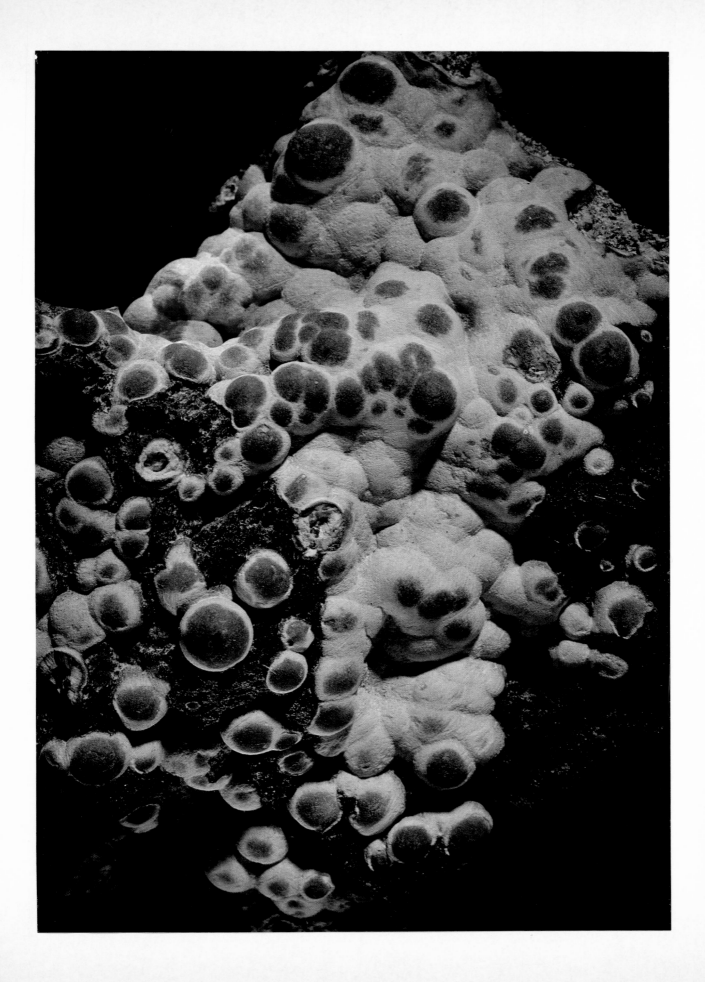

62 ADAMITE. Aggregates of bluish-green crystals on the earthy limonite lining cavities in yellowish limestone ▪ From Laurion, Attica, Greece ▪ Named after the French mineralogist Adam ▪ $Zn_2[OH/AsO_4]$, orthorhombic ▪ Scale 2:1

chalcopyrite, blende, silver ores and even native silver. Ammonites from the Jurassic rocks are often preserved as pyrite. If wood is replaced by silica, it forms wood agate. A mineral with an entirely organic origin is *amber*, being the fossil resin from coniferous trees.

When a rock is broken up by weathering and borne away, it sometimes happens that the very heavy minerals remain behind. Running water, ocean currents and wind may be responsible for the concentration of heavy minerals by carrying away the fragments of all the lighter minerals. Such residual deposits of heavy minerals are called *placer deposits*. The placers of gold and platinum contain rounded grains of these precious metals. The gold in placer deposits may be in the form of small spangles or may occur as larger nuggets. Another metal found in commercial quantities in placer deposits is tin. Many placer deposits of precious stones, particularly of diamonds, have long been famous as the source of large and perfect specimens. The reason for this is that only the minerals free from cracks and other imperfections can withstand the constant collisions with other pebbles and grains in a river or stream. The gemstones obtained from placer deposits include diamond, zircon, sapphire, ruby, topaz, tourmaline and garnet.

Sedimentary rocks form only a very small proportion of the earth's crust, but on the actual surface of the crust both loose and consolidated sediments are very extensively developed. In spite of this, it is rare to find well-developed minerals in sediments, although occasionally druses containing good crystals may be present. Good crystals of pyrite, chalcopyrite or gypsum are sometimes formed in soft fine grained sedimentary rock. In the cavities within fossils very well-developed crystals may sometimes be present, and a number of minerals have been found replacing fossil shells. Concretions of marcasite are frequently found in clay and marl (Plate 44), and pyrite crystal-

63 STIBNITE. Felted mass of long steel-grey prisms with metallic lustre, encrusted with yellow and ochre oxides of antimony and associated with crystals of quartz to the right ▪ From Felsöbanya, South-East Carpathians, Hungary ▪ Name from Latin *stibium*—antimony ▪ Sb_2S_3, orthorhombic ▪ Scale 3:1

lises in the course of time in sediments formed of putrid mud and in coal. Native *sulphur* may be formed in a number of ways: as a deposit around volcanic craters and near sulphurous springs; by the action of sulphur bacteria; and by the reduction of sulphates such as gypsum and anhydrite by organic substances. Smaller quantities of sulphur are also formed in the oxidation zone of sulphide-ore bodies. The reduction of sedimentary rocks containing sulphide minerals has led to the formation of commercially important ore deposits, which also contain the finest and largest crystals of native sulphur (Plate 1).

Minerals precipitated from solution as a result of evaporation of marine or inland waters are called *evaporites*. In the deposits formed in the open sea, rock-salt is always the predominant mineral, but in land-locked seas and inland lakes in hot desert and steppe areas the evaporation of water results in the precipitation of a much larger range of saline minerals.

Rivers are constantly carrying into the sea large quantities of dissolved salts obtained from the chemical weathering of rocks. Salts are also brought to the surface by volcanoes. The salt content of the oceans is thus constantly increasing, since only a very small proportion of it is deposited on the ocean bed. If the waters of the oceans were completely evaporated away, leaving the salt deposited as a layer of even thickness over the ocean floors and continents, this would form a crust 120 feet thick. The most abundant salt in marine salt deposits is *rock-salt*—the only mineral which is regularly consumed by humans in its natural state. The blue colour of the rock-salt cube is due to atomic radiation within the mineral (Plate 45). Salt is obtained commercially either by the mining of solid salt deposits or by the evaporation of brines or seawater in salt-pans in regions with a hot climate.

130

64 GARNIERITE. Coarsely nodular aggregate of fine-grained apple-green crystals, the surface in places coated with limonite ▪ From Noumea, New Caledonia, South Pacific ▪ Named after its French discoverer Garnier ▪ $(Ni, Mg)_6[(OH)_8/Si_4O_{10}]$, monoclinic ▪ Scale 2·2:1

Some saline minerals are stable only in a dry atmosphere and deliquesce if an appreciable amount of water vapour is present. It is thus important to keep specimens of hydroscopic salts in dry show cases or desiccators.

6. Minerals in the Zones of Oxidation and Cementation of Sulphide Ore Deposits

Ore deposits lying close to the surface are usually affected by weathering, whereupon new minerals are formed. When ores containing pyrite and other iron-rich sulphides are weathered, deposits of limonite and ferric oxide are formed. These deposits are sometimes called *iron cap*, and the term *cap deposits* is often used to describe the oxidised ores of all sulphide bodies.

In the zone of weathering, the ore content of many veins is decomposed and dissolved and the material is re-deposited in the form of fresh minerals which are chemically stable under the new conditions. In the higher part of the zone, which is known as the *zone of oxidation*, the sulphide and arsenide ores are oxidised and dissolved; the solutions so formed percolate downwards and fresh minerals may be precipitated just below the water-table. In this way a *zone of cementation*, often called the *enriched zone*, is formed below the water-table, where copper and silver ores, as well as native gold and newly-formed sulphide ores, may be found. As a result of this downward percolation, a zone of mineral enrichment may be produced containing valuable metals that were originally in parts of the crust which have long since been removed by denudation. The ore content of many unweathered mineral veins or lodes is so small as to make their exploitation an uneconomic proposition, but the deposits in the zone of cementation of an ore province are usually

65 ANDALUSITE (Chiastolite). This variety of andalusite shows in cross-section the twinned crystals with black inclusions segregated along the junction planes between them, producing the characteristic cruciform shape ▪ From Gefrees, Bavaria ▪ Andalusite named after its occurrence in Andalusia ▪ Chiastolite named after the cross-shaped inclusions, which resemble the Greek letter χ (chi) ▪ $Al_2[O/SiO_4]$, orthorhombic ▪ Scale 7·2:1

large and sufficiently rich in ores to be of economic value. As the more unstable minerals are decomposed and dissolved out, the mineral veins in the zone of oxidation usually acquire a cellular, spongy or scoriaceous appearance. In the cavities fine crystals of new minerals may, however, be formed. Very large zones of secondary sulphide enrichment occur in areas with a dry, warm climate, where the solutions of decomposed minerals are not too rapidly diluted and carried away by rain. In areas of heavy rainfall the zones of weathering in ore provinces are often extensively leached out and are virtually devoid of oxidised minerals. Another important factor influencing the type of new minerals formed is the character of the country rock. Acid solutions of weathered minerals, for instance, react readily with limestones and other rocks rich in carbonate to form a number of new minerals. In the zone of weathering minerals are often transported and re-deposited in solution, and the country rock may be impregnated with minerals.

Both in sedimentary rocks and in cap deposits, *pseudomorphs* are commonly found. These are crystals of one mineral which have the shape of another whose place they have taken. There are various types of pseudomorphs with fine crystal shapes which are much sought after by collectors. The original mineral is usually replaced by the new mineral at the same time as it is being dissolved, and its original shape is perfectly preserved. In some cases, the mineral being pseudomorphed is changed into a new mineral of similar composition by the partial substitution of certain elements in the lattice. In other pseudomorphs the original mineral is first encrusted by, or enclosed in, another mineral, and may then be dissolved out completely. If the space so formed is not re-filled by some other mineral substance, the hollow is called a negative pseudomorph.

134

66 RHODONITE. Streaky rose-red polished plate with the cracks filled with manganese oxides ▪ From Happy Camp, Siskiyou County, California, U.S.A. ▪ Name from Greek *rhodon*—rose—because of its colour ▪ (Mn, Fe, Ca) [SiO$_3$], triclinic ▪ Scale 1·5:1

Colloidal minerals of nodular shape formed from glutinous mineral gels are characteristically developed in the zone of weathering of ore deposits. Surface waters rich in oxygen are often involved in their formation. Such colloidal minerals, which usually become crystalline in time, are recognised by their nodular, reniform or botryoidal shape and their bright lustrous surface (Plates 48, 52).

The minerals formed in the zone of cementation are predominantly oxides and hydroxides, but also include carbonates, sulphates, phosphates, arsenates, molybdates, chromates, wolframates vanadates and other salts. These minerals not only occur as aggregates but may also form perfect crystals. The local climate, the nature of the original ore minerals, the character of the country rock and other factors, such as the presence of sea-water in the zone, all influence the character of the minerals formed. They may be multi-coloured, massive, granular, radiating, foliaceous, lamellar, botryoidal or earthy masses, or may form thin incrustations or films. Powdery, earthy masses formed by the decomposition of iron ores are usually termed ochres. Antimony ochre, for example, is a powdery, encrusting mineral aggregate, composed of the minerals cervantite, hydroromeite and stibioconite, which are products of the oxidation of antimony ores (Plate 63). Hydrated sulphates of minerals are often called vitriols, the best known of which are copper vitriol and iron vitriol (Plate 53). Both are characteristically developed in the zone of weathering in regions with a warm, dry climate.

The oxidised ores of many ore deposits include numerous, often remarkably colourful, minerals. In many instances the presence of these highly-coloured and striking oxidised minerals has led to the discovery of rich ore deposits below. Very often, however, the oxidised minerals were, in the

136

67 LAPIS LAZULI. Deep azure-blue grains, with yellow crystals of pyrite, embedded in white marble ▪
From Malaya Bistraya, Lake Baikal, U.S.S.R. ▪ Name from Latin *lapis*—stone—and Arabic *azul*—blue—because
of its colour ▪ $(Na, Ca)_8[(SO_4, S, Cl)_2/(AlSiO_4)_6]$, cubic ▪ Pyrite, FeS_2, cubic ▪ Scale 1·4:1

early days of mining, in greater demand than the underlying unweathered minerals, as the former could be more easily smelted. The primitive techniques of smelting were suitable for the extraction of cap deposits but could not cope with the underlying sulphide ores. Smithsonite, the zinc carbonate, for instance, was mined by the ancients, whereas blende, which weathers to form smithsonite in the zone of oxidation, has only been important as a zinc ore since the beginning of the last century.

Often the colour of the oxidised varieties is enough to tell us what types of unweathered minerals can be expected below. Particularly bright variegated minerals are formed during the weathering of pitchblende and other uranium minerals. Blue and green are characteristic of the copper-bearing minerals in this zone. Green malachite (Plates 9, 50, 55), green chrysocolla (Plate 52), green phosphochalcite (Plate 56), blue azurite and blue copper vitriol or chalcanthite (Plate 53) are examples. Malachite is formed by the weathering of various copper ores, particularly chalcopyrite. It forms infillings of thin fissures and covers the adjoining rock with pale green films, often giving the impression of a much greater quantity of copper ore than there really is.

If the unweathered copper minerals contain arsenic, as is the case with tetrahedrite and enargite, the weathering product is usually azurite. The dark blue azurite is, like malachite, a hydrated copper carbonate, and, also like malachite, it may form good crystals or crusty aggregates, or occur as reniform or botryoidal nodules with a radially fibrous internal structure. Oxidised copper ore sometimes occurs as a brown or brownish-black earthy or dense mass made up of various copper minerals, such as red cuprite together with limonite (Plate 50). Phosphochalcite, or pseudomalachite, is formed by the action of solutions containing phosphates on weathering copper ores. This

68 CLINOCHLORE. Thick concertina-like, often curved aggregates of tabular crystals, associated with translucent red crystals of hessonite (calcium-aluminium garnet) ▪ From Mussa Alps, Piedmont, Italy ▪ Name clinochlore from Greek *clino*—I bend—because of the crystal form, and Greek *chloros*—greenish-yellow—because of its colour ▪ $Mg_5Al[(OH)_8/AlSi_3O_{10}]$, monoclinic ▪ Hessonite named after Greek *hesson*—inferior—because it is less valuable than the zircon hyacinth, which it resembles ▪ $Ca_3Al_2[SiO_4]_3$, cubic ▪ Scale 2·6:1

dark pistachio-green mineral forms incrustations or felted aggregates composed of thin needle-like crystals (Plate 56). The green mineral chrysocolla (Plate 52)—like the much rarer emerald-green dioptase (emerald copper), which is sometimes used as a gemstone—is formed from copper-bearing solutions rich in silica. The pale green mineral torbernite (Plate 57), a uranium-bearing mica, also contains copper. Other minerals, such as adamite, a zinc arsenate (Plate 62), may owe their green colour to small traces of copper.

Lead is present in a number of coloured well-crystallised minerals occurring in the zone of oxidation. Many lead ores used to be named after their colour, as, for instance, white lead ore (cerussite), blue lead (galena), red oxide of lead (minium) and green lead ore (pyromorphite and mimetite). Many lead ores belonging to the zone of weathering may form incrustations on partially weathered primary lead ores, or may fill cavities in partially dissolved galena, where they may give rise to good crystals. Pyromorphite, which is frequently grass-green, may form groups of barrel-shaped, prismatic or needle-shaped crystals (Plate 58). Crystals of wulfenite (Plate 59) are either platy or form short pyramids, and quite often thin platy crystals are intergrown to make fine crystal groups. Wulfenite may be yellow or orange, or, more commonly, lemon- to wax-yellow. Crocoite is a chromate of lead, and is composed of elements which usually crystallise out under quite different geochemical conditions. Chromium minerals are generally among the first to crystallise from a magmatic melt, whereas lead is deposited by residual hydrothermal solutions. Crocoite is thus only developed when solutions formed by the weathering of galena or other lead ores come into contact with country rock containing chrome minerals.

A large number of minerals in the zones of oxidation and cementation are formed through the

69 RUBY. Blood-red corundum encrusted with minute crystals of green zoisite, and a cut ruby showing colour zoning which emphasizes its trigonal symmetry ▪ From Longido, Tanganyka ▪ Name ruby from Latin *rubeus*— red—and name corundum from its Sanskrit name *kuruwinda* ▪ Al_2O_3, the red colour due to minute traces of chromium, hexagonal ▪ Zoisite named after the Austrian Baron von Zois ▪ $Ca_2Al_3[O/OH/SiO_4/Si_2O_7]$, orthorhombic ▪ Scale 1·2 : 1

weathering of *zinc* ores, particularly blende. The reaction of zinc-bearing solutions with limestone forms smithsonite, the zinc carbonate. This mineral occurs as small, grey, generally densely packed crystals, or as scaly or nodular aggregates which are often coloured by traces of another substance (Plate 61). Aggregates of smithsonite and other oxygen-rich zinc minerals like hemimorphite and hydrozincite are sometimes called *calamine*. The mineral *adamite* may be formed when arsenic-bearing solutions come into contact with zinc minerals. Adamite occurs either in finely crystalline aggregates of nodular or stalactitic shape, or forms bluish-green crystals with a glassy lustre and tabular habit, often arranged in wart-shaped groups (Plate 62).

The most common and important cap deposit of all is *limonite*, the hydrated iron oxide (Plate 48). Though limonite can be formed from juvenile solutions of magmatic origin, it is most commonly precipitated from solutions which have seeped downwards from the surface. In some cases limonite may have been precipitated in areas where surface waters and juvenile solutions were intermixed. In the zones of weathering limonite is often dissolved out and re-deposited elsewhere. The mineral can appear in a large number of different forms, sometimes bearing separate names.

Many ore minerals belonging to the zone of weathering are very colourful, but some deliquesce readily, merely on exposure to damp fresh air. The minerals most affected are those which are formed as stalactites by dripping water. In order to preserve the colours of these mineral aggregates, it is essential that they should be stored or exhibited in sealed cases or desiccators. The number and variety of minerals found in the zone of weathering is completely unrelated to the number of ore and gangue minerals in the original deposit. Many ore deposits having only a small number of primary ores may contain many fine minerals in their weathered zone.

70 SAPPHIRE. Water-worn blue corundum crystal of barrel-shaped habit from a gemstone placer deposit ▪ From Ceylon ▪ Name probably from the island *Sapphirine* in the Arabian Sea ▪ Al_2O_3, the blue colour due to traces of iron and titanium, hexagonal ▪ Scale 1·5 : 1

7. Minerals of Metamorphic Origin

Metamorphism, the changing of minerals and rocks, may take place in the deeper parts of the earth's crust as a consequence of rising temperature and pressure. In many cases metamorphism is directly connected with the emplacement of large bodies of plutonic rock or with major earth movements. Metamorphism affects both igneous and sedimentary rocks, and rocks already metamorphosed may be further altered. Schists and gneisses formed by the alternation of igneous rocks are called orthogneisses or orthoschists, and those formed by the alteration of sediments are paragneisses or paraschists. During the metamorphism of some rocks the existing minerals may remain. For example, when pure limestone is changed to marble, the calcite crystals are merely re-crystallised. More commonly, however, the metamorphism of rocks involves not merely a change in the size and shape of grains but also the growth of new minerals and the disappearance of some of the original ores.

In many instances the over-all chemical composition of a rock is not altered through metamorphism, but quite frequently there is an exchange of material with the outside, so that the total composition of the rock undergoes some change. During this process, material is transported in the water which fills joints and pore spaces in the rock, and in some instances forms a capillary layer around individual grains. Exchange of material in the solid state may also play an important part in the reaction.

If the rocks are being altered by stress only, the individual minerals are first deformed plastically; but if certain stress limits are exceeded, they are intensely fractured, the process being known as

71 ACTINOLITE. Long dark green prismatic crystals embedded in yellowish-brown mica-schist ▪ From Greiner, Zillertal, Tyrol, Austria ▪ Name from Greek *aktis*—ray—and *lithos*—stone ▪ $Ca_2(Mg, Fe)_5[(OH)_2/(Si_4O_{11})_2]$, monoclinic ▪ Scale 1·5:1

cataclasis. In such rocks new minerals may be formed by re-crystallisation, and the joints and cracks in the rock are often filled with calcite, silica or serpentine. If the rock is sheared and broken up even more severely and crushed into rock flour, the resulting product is called *mylonite*.

If metamorphism affects a very large area, we speak of *regional metamorphism*. This is usually connected with major mountain-building movements and the emplacement of large granitic plutons. Metamorphism resulting mainly from more superficial earth movements in which tectonic stresses only are involved is termed *dynamic metamorphism*. Rocks may also be metamorphosed solely by the weight of a great thickness of overlying sediments.

In an area which has undergone regional metamorphism, the rocks range from types altered relatively little, such as slate, to such intensely metamorphosed rocks as granite-gneiss. There are thus a number of *grades* or *zones*, and these can be recognised by the presence of certain mineral associations. In the Scottish Highlands, six such zones, named after a characteristic mineral, are recognised.

The least altered rocks belong to the *chlorite zone* and include the slates and phyllites. The latter are very fissile rocks with slightly wavy surfaces having a silky sheen. Newly-formed minerals in rocks of this zone are chlorite, serizite, albite and zoisite. The second zone is the *biotite zone*, in which once clayey rocks are converted into mica schists, the chlorite being changed to biotite, serizite and muscovite. Like the phyllites, the mica schists consist of platy minerals with parallel alignment. With more intense metamorphism, new minerals appear. The schists in the third zone, the *garnet zone*, contain well-formed crystals of garnet, and in the fourth zone, the *staurolite zone*,

72 STAUROLITE. Right-angled penetration twin ▪ From Morganton, Georgia, U.S.A. ▪ Name from Greek *stauros*—cross—and *lithos*—stone ▪ $Al_4Fe[O/OH/SiO_4]_2$, orthorhombic ▪ Scale 5·1 :1

73 STAUROLITE. Oblique-angled penetration twin ▪ From Quimper, Brittany, France ▪ $Al_4Fe[O/OH/SiO_4]_2$, orthorhombic ▪ Scale 2·2: 1

staurolite and kyanite make their appearance. Staurolite crystals (Plates 72, 73) often form characteristic cross-like penetration twins. The zone of most intense metamorphism is the *sillimanite zone*, taking in the new minerals sillimanite and cordierite. Other minerals which were formed by re-crystallisation in the more highly metamorphosed rocks are feldspars, pyroxenes, amphiboles, various garnets and spinel.

It has been suggested that the degree of metamorphism is determined by the depth within the earth's crust at which rocks were metamorphosed, and the German geologist Grubenman recognised three depth zones as follows: the *epi-zone*, composed of rocks of low metamorphic grade which were altered at shallow depth; the *meso-zone*, containing the more highly metamorphosed rocks formed at intermediate depths; and the *kata-zone*, consisting of the most intensely metamorphosed rocks which re-crystallised at great depths.

A characteristic feature of the *structure* or *fabric* of many metamorphic rocks is the parallel alignment of the platy minerals. This structure, known as *foliation*, was developed during the re-crystallisation of the metamorphic rocks, and is not related to the bedding of the sedimentary rocks from which they may have been formed. In phyllites, mica-schists, gneisses and other metamorphic rocks, the platy minerals were rotated during deformation so that their flat surfaces came to lie at right angles to the direction of maximum pressure.

The various rock types react to the different physical conditions which may prevail during metamorphism in diverse ways. For instance, the deep-seated igneous rocks which were formed at high temperatures and pressures are much less affected by a rise in temperature than,

148

74 ROCK-CRYSTAL. Quartz with minute included scales of chlorite which in the upper crystal reveal the zoning and earlier growth stages ▪ From Riental, near Göschenen, Switzerland ▪ Name chlorite from Greek *chloros*—greenish-yellow ▪ Approximately $(Mg, Fe, Al)_6 [(OH)_8/(Al, Si)_4 O_{10}]$, monoclinic ▪ Rock-crystal, SiO_2, hexagonal ▪ Scale 2·4 : 1

say, the sulphide ore minerals, though these in turn are less vulnerable than the saline minerals. In the case of very intensely metamorphosed rocks it is often difficult to tell what they were like originally. Sometimes relicts or trace minerals, which may have got through the metamorphism unchanged, may give some indication. The determination of the original rock type is, however, made more difficult by the fact that many identical metamorphic rocks are formed from quite different parent rocks. Mudstones and basalts, for example, can both be converted into amphibolites, and gneisses of identical composition and texture may have been derived from granite, rhyolitic lava or feldspathic sandstone. Coal, when intensely metamorphosed, is converted into graphite, but this mineral may also occur in pegmatites. Bauxite can be converted into emery. Epidote, serpentine, talc and the various asbestos minerals can derive from a variety of rock types. A considerable number of minerals are found only in metamorphic rocks. Examples are tremolite, actinolite, glaucophane, staurolite, kyanite, sillimanite, wollastonite, scapolite, cordierite, nephrite and jadeite. On the other hand, minerals which occur in igneous rocks, such as sanidine, leucite, the feldspathoids, melilite and the orthorhombic pyroxenes, as well as the mineral glasses, are not usually found in metamorphic rocks.

We have seen that there is a gradual transition from the magmatic to the pegmatitic, pneumatolitic and, eventually, hydrothermal phases of crystallisation in magmatic rocks. There is an equally gradual transition between processes of rock formation which can be described as sedimentary and metamorphic. For instance, the cementation and secondary mineral growth in newly formed sediments, which is concerned with the formation of sedimentary rocks, is really a metamorphic process.

Rocks metamorphosed under high pressure never have open cavities, but they may, nevertheless, contain well-developed crystals. During intense metamorphism, certain mineral species are able, as a result of mineral accretion, to develop idiomorphic crystals. During the growth of these minerals, small grains of other minerals are enclosed in the growing crystal, and the remaining rock is literally pushed aside. Minerals which form such perfect crystals, known an *idioblasts*, are garnet, hornblende, magnetite, biotite, chlorite, albite, staurolite, tourmaline, rutile, kyanite, epidote and zoisite. Particularly large and well-developed crystals of this type, called *porphyroblasts*, are grown when transfer of material by permeation takes place at the same time as the metamorphism of the rock.

When rocks are changed by intense heat in the proximity of igneous intrusions, we talk of *thermal*, or *contact*, metamorphism. The intensity and extent of thermal metamorphism depend on the difference in the temperature of the intruding magma and the adjoining rock, on the difference in the chemical composition of the two adjoining media, and, not least, on the duration of the rise in temperature. Few minerals may thus form when a stream of lava flows over sediments and consolidates rapidly. The adjoining sediment undergoes very little change in this event. When large magmatic bodies are intruded into sedimentary rocks, a wide zone of alteration, known as the *metamorphic aureole*, may be formed. In this zone, sedimentary minerals are changed into forms which are stable at the new temperatures. New minerals formed during the thermal metamorphism of rocks composed largely of clay minerals are andalusite and chiastolite (Plate 65). The intensely altered rock formed on actual contact between the sedimentary and intrusive rock, where the thermal metamorphism was most intense, is known as hornfels. A manganese silicate resulting

76 ADULARIA. Crystal carrying a rosette of haematite, the whole encrusted with chlorite ▪ From Wassen, Uri Canton, Switzerland ▪ Named after *Mons Adula*, the Latin name for the St Gotthard ▪ $K[(Si, Al)_4 O_8]$, monoclinic ▪ Chlorite, approximately $(Mg, Fe, Al)_6 [(OH)_8/(Al, Si)_4 O_{10}]$, monoclinic ▪ Haematite, $Fe_2 O_3$, hexagonal ▪ Scale 4·4:1

from metamorphism in the zone of contact is the rose-red rhodonite, which is often traversed by cracks filled with black manganese oxides and hydroxides (Plate 66). A mineral of rarer occurrence in this zone is the azure-blue lapis lazuli (Plate 67).

During intense thermal metamorphism, sandstone changes to quartzite, shale to a hard spotted or hornfelsed rock, marl to calc-silicate hornfels, and dolomite to a magnesium silicate hornfels containing a large number of minerals.

If the intrusive magma comes into contact with sediments containing a large quantity of water, this is converted into superheated steam, which may carry away in solution various mineral substances and re-deposit them in a cooler area some distance away. If the cooling magma is itself giving off gases and other volatile substances, these may permeate into the adjoining rock and give rise to contact-pneumatolitic mineral associations. During contact-metamorphism some material may also pass from the heated country rock into the magma, and as a result unusual minerals may be formed in the intrusion.

Rare minerals are often found in thermally metamorphosed coal-bearing sediments, saline deposits and sulphide ores formed in the weathered zones of sulphide ore veins. Other unusual mineral assemblages are formed if there has been an active interchange of material between the magma and the country rock, or if the residual magmatic solutions penetrate into the adjoining country rock. Metamorphic rocks in the older tectonic belts have often been subjected to more than one period of metamorphism. Such rocks are termed *polymetamorphic*. If the various phases of re-crystallisation of these rocks have been very intense, it is not possible to ascertain the character of the original

rock. Rocks of a high metamorphic grade may be affected by a period of less intense metamorphism

and develop structures and minerals characteristic of a lower grade. This process, known as *retrograde metamorphism*, may, for example, change biotite back into an aggregate of chlorite minerals. If highly metamorphosed rocks are pushed into the deeper parts of the earth's crust, or if they are intensely permeated by granitic solutions, they may become fluid and pass into the magmatic state, or they may be converted into a rock of granitic aspect without actually melting. This latter process has been called *magmatisation* or *granitisation*, and rocks which are transitional between plutonic and metamorphic rocks are known as *magmatites*. The partial or complete fusion, or *mobilisation*, of metamorphic rocks in the deeper parts of the crust is called *rheomorphism*.

An extremely large variety of rock types with an almost limitless number of mineral combinations can thus be formed by the diverse processes of metamorphism.

8. Minerals in Alpine Joints and Fissures

The perfect crystals so frequently found in joints and fissures in the Alps and other recent mountain chains have always fascinated mineralogists and collectors. Very many different minerals with a surprisingly large variety of crystal forms are encountered.

The minerals in these fissures were deposited by aqueous solutions which dissolved out mineral substances from veins and druses in the adjoining rock. The joints and fissures were formed during the latest Alpine earth movements and filled with water that had been heated in the deeper parts of the crust and then percolated upwards. The mineralising solutions usually contained dissolved

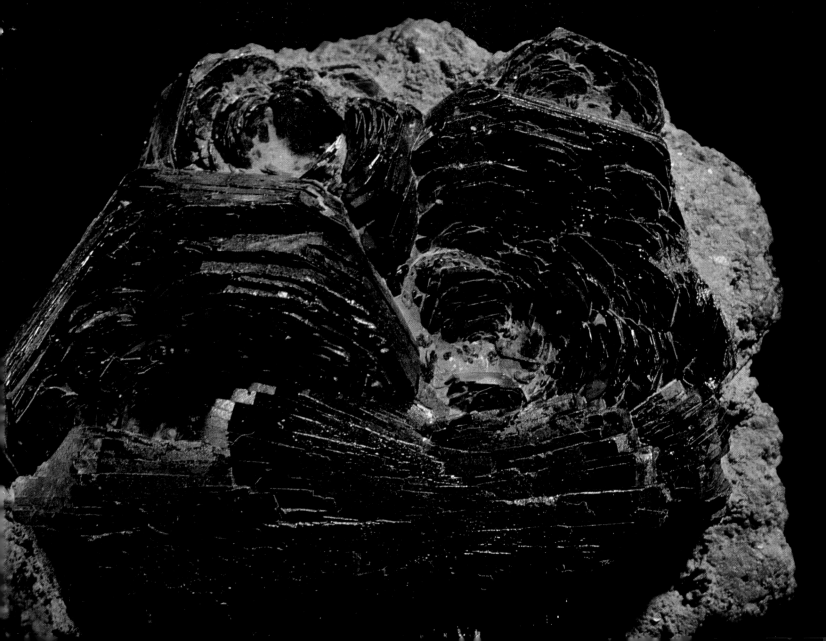

78 FLUORITE (Fluorspar). Group of transparent pink octahedral crystals ▪ From Grimsel in the St Gotthard region, Switzerland ▪ Name from Latin *fluor*—liquid—because it was used as a flux in ore smelting ▪ CaF_2, cubic ▪ Scale 3·4 : 1

carbon dioxide and reacted with the rock adjoining the fissures and cavities, carrying away soluble minerals in solution. With falling temperature the various minerals re-crystallised from the liquid. The kinds of mineral assemblages to be found in Alpine fissures are thus to a large extent controlled by the nature of the adjoining rocks.

In the Alpine countries many enthusiastic collectors of these fine minerals are still to be found. Professional mineral collectors usually know many out-of-the-way veins, some of which are in almost inaccessible places among the peaks. Moreover, a certain amount of risk is involved in the search for these minerals, as some of the best veins are on steep rock faces, in the path of avalanches, in scree-filled gulleys or among the permanent snow-fields. Not only is it difficult to find and open a mineral-bearing fissure, but the fragile minerals have then to be carried down into the valley. Some of the larger fissures may contain many hundredweights of rock-crystal and other minerals. The rarer minerals and really good crystals, however, are usually found in smaller joints and druses.

The most common and characteristic mineral of Alpine clefts is *rock-crystal* (Plates 6, 74, 75), which sometimes forms single crystals up to 3 feet long and over 200 lb. in weight. Particularly large and well-formed crystals from famous mineral veins have even been given individual names. Coloured varieties of quartz are smoky quartz, which is smoky brown or brownish-black and is often found in the higher regions of the Alps, and cairngorm, a smoky yellow to brown variety which used to be plentiful in the Cairngorm Mountains of Scotland. The intensely black variety of smoky quartz is called morion.

Rock-crystal from the Alpine clefts usually takes the form of prisms, but may also occur in many

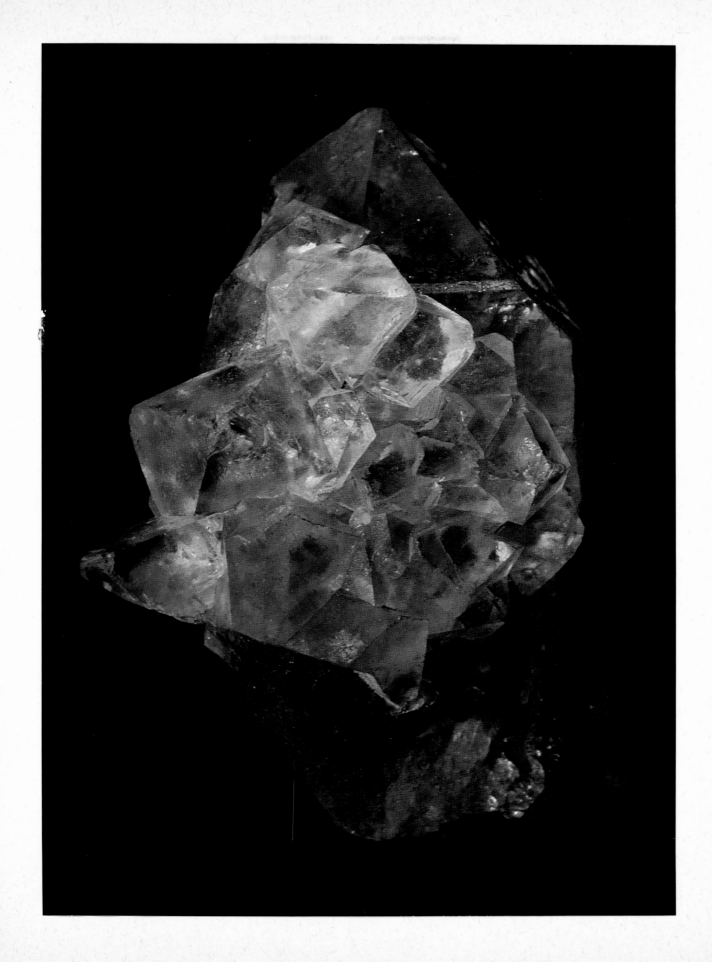

79 AMIANTHUS (Byssolite). Matted golden needles of actinolite asbestos on rock-crystals ▪ From Rotlaui-tal, Bernese Oberland, Switzerland ▪ Name amianthus from Greek *amiantos*—unsoiled—because the fibres could not be dyed ▪ Byssolite from Greek *byssos*—fine linen—and *lithos*—stone ▪ Approximately $Na_2Ca_4(Mg, Fe)_{10}$ $[(OH)_2O_2/(Si_4O_{11})_4]$, monoclinic ▪ Name actinolite from Greek *aktis*—ray—and *lithos*—stone ▪ $Ca_2(Mg, Fe)_5$ $[(OH)_2/(Si_4O_{11})_2]$, monoclinic ▪ Scale 2·4:1

other crystal shapes. Distorted forms and crystals twinned according to a number of laws, as well as irregularly intergrown crystal groups, are common. Spiral or curved specimens of rock-crystal are usually made up of a large number of crystals which are intergrown according to certain definite laws. The skeletal form of rock-crystal known as *window puartz* (Plate 75) is a more unusual type.

The various mineral assemblages of Alpine fissures include adularia (Plate 76), albite, pericline, sphene (Plate 80) and chlorite (Plate 82). Adularia is a glassy, lustrous variety of orthoclase. Frequently crystals or twins of adularia are encrusted with a layer of chlorite. *Axinite*, which is a boron mineral, is usually found in fissures in contact-pneumatolitic calc-silicate rocks. Here it usually takes the form of brown wedge-shaped crystals with extremely sharp edges (Plate 82). *Sphene*, which also occurs in a number of igneous rocks, forms intergrown crystals which have a flat, tabular shape looking rather like an envelope. The freely growing sphene crystals in Alpine fissures can have a number of distinct shapes, usually with a tabular or prismatic habit, and are frequently twinned (Plate 80). *Haematite* (Plates 76, 77) may occur in tabular crystals intergrown in such a way as to form rosettes. Haematite of this type usually contains a small percentage of titanium. The leek- or dark-green minerals of the *chlorite* family are commonly found in Alpine fissures. They give rise to fine, scaly aggregates which may occur as films over quartz and other minerals, as inclusions in other minerals or as a basal layer from which the projecting minerals have grown (Plates 74, 76, 80, 82). They often form a thin film on the walls of the fissures, and sometimes occur as friable 'chlorite sand' occupying small cavities. Only rarely do the chlorite minerals penninite and clinochlore (Plate 68) form separate crystals of appreciable size.

80 TITANITE (Sphene). Translucent yellowish-brown penetration twin formed of elongated monoclinic crystals, on green chlorite and itself dusted with fine green chlorite ▪ From Valle Maggia, Ticino, Switzerland ▪ Name sphene from Greek *sphen*—wedge—because of the wedge-shaped crystal form ▪ Name titanite, because of its content of titanium, named after the *Titans* of Greek Mythology ▪ $CaTi[O/SiO_4]$, monoclinic ▪ Chlorite, approximately $(Mg, Fe, Al)_6 [(OH)_8/(Al, Si)_4 O_{10}]$, monoclinic ▪ Scale 3·6:1

The fibrous or matted asbestiform varieties of the mineral actinolite, such as *amianthus* and *byssolite* (Plate 79), have sometimes been called mountain cork, mountain leather or mountain wood, depending on the extent of matting of the fibres. These unusual mineral aggregates, which are quite frequently flexible, are composed of many hair-like crystals of actinolite.

Mineralised fissures in the Calcareous Alps usually contain water-clear crystals of calcite and dolomite. Among the rarer minerals of Alpine fissures is *fluorspar*, which forms fine crystals of octahedral habit (Plate 78). In just a few of the fissures one may find the gleaming red calcium-aluminium garnet, *hessonite*, which has a resinous lustre (Plate 68). Very fine specimens of hessonite associated with clinochlore or other chlorite minerals, and sometimes also with diopside, may be found in fissures in chlorite-schist or slate. Groups of sulphide minerals with good crystals of, say, *blende* (Plate 81) may be formed under certain circumstances in Alpine fissures.

9. Extra-Terrestrial Minerals

Meteorites are solid bodies which enter the earth's atmosphere from outer space. Small meteorites usually burn out and disintegrate in the atmosphere. Larger cosmic bodies are heated during their journey through the atmosphere, with the result that a thin outer skin usually starts to glow and is melted, although the core may not be greatly heated. According to their composition, these extra-terrestrial bodies can be grouped into *stony* and *iron* meteorites. The former appear to be derived from the silicate-rich crusts of disintegrated cosmic bodies, whereas the latter may be portions of the core of such bodies. Intermediate between the stony and iron meteorites are the

81 SPHALERITE (Blende). Golden-brown translucent tabular crystal on white granular dolomite containing a little pyrite ▪ From Lengenbach, near Imfeld, Binntal, Switzerland ▪ Name blende from German mining term meaning blind or deceptive, because of its resemblance to galena ▪ ZnS, cubic ▪ Dolomite, CaMg(CO$_3$)$_2$, hexagonal ▪ Pyrite, FeS$_2$, cubic ▪ Scale 6·6:1

so-called *pallasites*, which are composed of nickel-iron with inclusions of roundish crystals of olivine and other minerals found in the stony meteorites (Plate 83). These olivine crystals have a pale core and a darker peripheral zone.

Moldavite is a volcanic glass of extra-terrestrial origin, pieces of which have been found near the River Vltava (Moldau) in Bohemia. It is thought that a meteor shower composed of droplets of glass about the size of hazel nuts once landed in this area. Moldavite is cut and polished as a gemstone, as is the olivine from the stony and pallisite meteorites.

Although all the elements so far encountered in meteorites are also found on the earth, they sometimes contain compounds which are not known on earth. The yellowish-grey substance schreibersite (Plate 83) is an example. Neither traces of organisms, nor substances whose presence might suggest the existence of life, have as yet been discovered in meteorites.

GEMSTONES

Gemstones are those minerals greatly valued because of their special optical properties which give great beauty to the cut and polished stone, their extreme hardness and resistance to abrasion, and also because of their rarity. Gemstones are cut into gems and ornaments, and are much used to adorn regalia, ecclesiastical robes, and so on. The stones of gemstone quality belonging to many mineral species have been given special names. The precious varieties of *beryl*, for instance, are *aquamarine* and *emerald*, those of *corundum* are *ruby* and *sapphire*, and the gemstone form of *olivine* is *chrysolite*. When the same mineral occurs in several different colours, a different name is usually

164

given to each variety. Tourmaline, for instance, may appear as black *schorl*, brown *dravite*, red transparent *rubellite*, peach-coloured *apyrite*, violet *siberite*, blue *indicolite* and colourless *achroite*. However, colour is not always a guide to the relative value of different varieties of gem minerals, though actual shades of colour may make quite a difference to the appearance of the stone. In many cases the strong, full-blooded colours are preferred, but in the case of the diamond the most valuable stones are clear and colourless.

The standard measure of weight for precious stones is the carat (1 carat = $^1/_5$ gram). The word carat comes from the East—the Arabic *qirat* and Greek *keration*—where it refers to the weight of the seed of the carob tree. Because of their remarkably constant weight these seeds or beans were used by the ancients for weighing gemstones. The Romans, similarly, measured the weight of gemstones in siliquae, *siliqua graeca* being their name for the carob plant.

Gemstones do not form special groups of minerals, nor is their chemical composition or atomic structure in any way distinctive. Most gemstones are single crystals, but some may consist of mineral aggregates, like lapis lazuli, or may be amorphous, like opal. Amber and jet are also classed as gemstones. These are not true minerals but organic products, as are pearls and coral.

The gemstones include minerals of very diverse origin. A precious stone which was formed at great depth is *diamond*, which is composed of a single element, pure crystalline carbon. Most diamonds were brought to the surface by volcanoes, whose lava consists of the basic rock kimberlite. The largest diamond ever found is the Cullinan, which came from South Africa, and weighed 3,106 carats before it was cut. Even so, it was only a fragment of a larger stone. The annual world output of diamonds is about 5,400 kilograms. One fifth of these stones are of gemstone quality,

166

83 PALLASITE. Cut and polished section of a meteorite, composed of brown roundish grains of olivine, many of them enveloped in a dark crust containing schreibersite and troilite, enclosed in meteoric nickel-iron ▪ Found at Springwater, Saskatchewan, Canada in 1931 ▪ Name meteorite from Greek *meteoros*—soaring in the air ▪ Pallasite, named after the explorer Pallas, transitional between stony and iron meteorite ▪ Schreibersite named after the mineralogist Schreiber ▪ (Fe, Ni, Co)$_3$P, tetragonal ▪ Troilite named after the Jesuit priest Troili ▪ FeS, hexagonal ▪ Scale 1·7:1

the remainder being used for industrial purposes. The most important sources of diamonds are in South and West Africa, the Soviet Union and Brazil. Other gemstones which were formed under conditions of great pressure and temperature are the blood-red magnesium garnet *pyrope*, formerly obtained in Bohemia, and the feldspar *labradorite*. Particularly fine pieces of labradorite are found on the coast of Labrador and on the island of St Paul; there are other important sources of the mineral in the U.S.A. and in Scandinavia (Plates 3, 14).

Pegmatites and pneumatolitic mineral deposits may yield *beryl*. In older days, spectacle lenses were made from transparent crystals of beryl. The gemstone varieties of this mineral include *aquamarine*, which is transparent and coloured sea-blue by traces of iron, and *morganite*, which is coloured rose-pink by lithium salts; but the most valuable form of beryl is the green *emerald*. The finest emeralds have for centuries been obtained in Colombia, and finely coloured stones are also found in the Ural Mountains. A rare variety of the mineral *chrysoberyl* is *alexandrite*; it is dull green in daylight and blood-red when seen by artificial light. Two clear varieties of the mineral *spodumene* have become popular in recent years. These are *kunzite*, which is pink to lilac, and *hiddenite*, which ranges in colour from yellowish- to bluish-green. Among the *tourmalines*, which occur in many colour varieties, the most valuable are the green, red and blue stones. Most tourmalines used as gemstones come from South-West Africa, Madagascar and Brazil. *Topaz*, besides assuming various shades of yellow, may also be colourless, pink, wine-red, and even blue. Good crystals with many faces are obtained in Brazil, Madagascar, South-West Africa, Ceylon and the U.S.A. *Zircon*, a zirconium silicate, only rarely forms crystals of gemstone quality. The most valuable are the bluish stones and the yellowish-red to red-brown variety known as *hyacinth*. The best hyacinths

168

84 VASE OF SARDONYX. Dating from the 8th century ▪ Funeral scene ▪ The neck has two rows of pearls and a central row of alternate sapphires and emeralds, and the base has two emerald-sapphire rows between rows of pearls. The sapphires and emeralds are of very variable size and quality ▪ Height of vase 9 in., height of sardonyx 6 in., maximum diameter 4⅓ in. ▪ Abbey of St Maurice, Switzerland

come from Siam, Indo-China and Ceylon. Perfect crystals of *rose-quartz*, which are transparent and free from cracks, are obtained in Brazil. The only potash feldspars used as gemstones are *adularia* and *moonstone*. The latter is milky white and has an iridescent sheen; the finest specimens of moonstone come from Ceylon.

Many of the gem varieties of silica are found in amygdales and other cavities in extrusive rocks. Of particular value are *amethyst* (Plate 2), and the varieties of chalcedony, which include *agate* and *onyx*. *Opal* is also commonly associated with volcanic rocks. As the Hungarian deposits of opal are now largely exhausted, the main present-day sources of this mineral are in Mexico and Australia. Fire-opal, the translucent variety with the red sheen, is obtained chiefly in Mexico.

One of the few gemstones found among hydrothermal mineral deposits is *bloodstone*, a form of haematite which, when cut and polished, has a lively, dark, steely lustre.

Jasper is one of the few gemstones of sedimentary origin. It forms white, grey, yellowish, brown and reddish varieties, some of which have been given special names. Like jasper, *carnelian* is an impure form of chalcedony. A gemstone which has been valued for centuries is *turquoise*, particularly the pale blue variety. Turquoise (Plate 60) usually forms irregular, platy or nodular aggregates, consisting of compactly intergrown grains. There are important sources of turquoise in Persia, Afghanistan, Tibet and New Mexico.

In the zones of oxidation of copper sulphide ore bodies, especially in the Ural Mountains, South-West Africa and the U.S.A., one finds the soft but highly valued mineral *malachite*. The banded specimens are particularly sought after, especially those with alternating pale and dark concentric layers (Plate 9). Aggregates consisting of alternate layers of malachite and azurite may display

170

a number of different structural patterns. *Chrysoprase* (Plate 39) is formed in areas where nickeli-
ferous serpentine is being weathered. The best specimens of this gemstone come from Silesia.
Among the large number of gemstones of metamorphic origin are the *spinels*, which may produce
red, purple or violet crystals. *Garnets* are found in a wide range of metamorphic rocks. The garnet
family comprises a large number of minerals with distinctive colours. These include *spessartite* (pale
orange); *grossularite* (transparent green); *demantoid* (iridescent green); *hessonite* (orange-brown),
(Plate 68); *melanite* (black); and *almandine* (wine-red to violet). *Ruby* and *sapphire* are *corundums*, the
one coloured red by chromium, the other blue by titanium and iron. The most valuable of these
are the blood-red rubies with a silky sheen and the cornflower-blue sapphires. The intriguing star of
light seen in the star rubies and star sapphires is due to the presence of small needle-like inclusions in
these stones. Both are found in Ceylon, Siam and Burma; fine sapphires are also obtained in
Kashmir and Australia. *Lapis lazuli* (Plate 67), which has been valued as a gemstone for thousands
of years, is found principally in Afghanistan. *Jade* is the name used for both *jadeite* and *nephrite*.
Although these are two completely different minerals—jadeite is a pyroxene and nephrite an
amphibole—they both form green, opaque, remarkably tough aggregates which are composed
essentially of very fine, completely felted fibres. Nephrite has a greater compressive strength than
steel, and in prehistoric times was for this reason a coveted raw material for tools and weapons.
Nearly all the nephrite comes from China; jadeite of gemstone quality from Burma and New
Zealand.

Pegmatites and Alpine fissures yield rock-crystal. This is hardly considered to be a gemstone at the
present day, but is increasingly used for industrial and scientific purposes.

GEMSTONES—THEIR HISTORY AND MYTHOLOGY

If gemstones are to be used for ornamental purposes, they have to be cut and polished so that their exceptional optical properties can be displayed to their greatest effect.

The carving of gemstones was first practised to an important extent in China, where jadeite, nephrite, agalmatolite and steatite, which are particularly suitable for carving, were available. The minerals were carved into amulets, statuettes, pagodas, receptacles, ear-rings, seals, sword and dagger handles and bracelets, many of which are admired as works of art to this day.

The art of carving stone—glyptography—was known and practised in ancient Egypt, where malachite, lapis lazuli and carnelian were carved into signet rings, amulets, scarabs and cameos. Carving was also practised in Mesopotamia. Herod reported that every Babylonian wore a signet ring carved out of lapis lazuli agate, carnelian or haematite. Beakers and bowls of obsidian and lazurite, animal amulets of lapis lazuli and flowers and bracelets of lapis lazuli and carnelian were made in Mesopotamia as early as 3200 B.C. The Egyptians also taught the art of carving gemstones to the inhabitants of Crete and Mycenae.

The Greeks in Asia Minor learned the art of gem-carving from the Orient, and they passed it on to the Etruscans. After the capture of Alexandria, which was then the centre of the Hellenic cameo manufacturing industry, Roman citizens developed a passion for cameos and brought to their capital the finest gem-carvers of the 'orbis terrarum'. There they produced, principally out of amethyst, carnelian, chalcedony and hyacinth, countless delightful cameos and intaglios (i.e. cameos with hollowed-out design).

87 CLEOPATRA BROOCH. Carving Italian, c. 1550, setting German, c. 1590 ▪ Gold-embossed half-length figure of Cleopatra pressing the asp to her bosom with her right hand; face and hands carved in hyacinth; head-dress, clothing and asp in glazed enamel inset with a diamond and emeralds; cloak is glazed in blue. Framed with lacework of enamel glazed in many colours and studded with diamonds, rubies and emeralds in rectangular settings ▪ 2¾ in. × 3⅓ in. ▪ Treasury, The Residenz, Munich

The art of gem-carving survived the decay of the Roman Empire and was still practised in the Italian city-states of the Middle Ages—Venice, Florence and Milan. To the north of the Alps there is evidence that gem-carving was carried on in Paris in 1352. In the 15th century the most important gem-carving centres were Vienna, Freiburg in the Black Forest, and Burgundy. Some very remarkable bowls, vases and beakers carved from rock-crystal date from this period.

The process of cutting and polishing gemstones appears to have originated in India. The Indian style of cutting sought to give the stone a large number of polished surfaces, known as facets, without losing more of the precious raw material than was absolutely necessary. Indian stones are thus readily recognised by their irregular shape. From India the art of gem-cutting reached the cultural centres of the Tigris and Euphrates and the Nile. Up to the 12th century, gem-cutting techniques in Europe were extremely primitive. The stones were cemented to a stick, rubbed by hand against a hard sandstone, and finally polished with a ground tile and saliva, either on a lead plate or on a stretched chamois leather.

After the capture of Asia Minor, Palestine and Egypt by the Romans, large quantities of gemstones of immense value and a great store of knowledge about gem-cutting techniques found their way to Rome. A similar influx of gemstones and knowledge followed the Crusades. Cut gemstones, together with their Indian, Persian and Arabic names, spread into western countries where they had hitherto been unknown, and the practice of gem-cutting and polishing gained a foothold in Central and Western Europe. From then on, shrines and jewel-cases, church apparatus and official insignia, weapons and bridles, bookbindings, clothes and vestments were artfully decorated with gemstones which were obtained from the Mediterranean countries.

176

88 LEPANTO MONSTRANCE. Gilded silver ▪ From the workshop of Johann Zeckl, Augsburg, 1708 ▪ Made for the Church of the Student Congregation of the University of Ingolstadt, Germany; Patron Saint Maria de Victoria; commemorates the victory of the Christians over the Turks in the sea-battle of Lepanto ▪ 58 gemstones and two pearls; the lunule contains two emeralds, four amethysts and one garnet; the corona around the lunule has 27 rubies, the figure of the Archangel Michael has one diamond and five rubies, and the figure of Maria de Victoria has one diamond, sixteen rubies and one garnet ▪ Height 4 ft. 6 in. ▪ Church of Maria de Victoria, Ingolstadt

Towards the end of the 13th century a thriving fraternity of *cristalliers* and *piesriers*—crystal and gem polishers—was operating in Paris. Not much later, lapidary centres were established in Rheims, Saint Denis and Metz. During the 14th century an important centre of the gem-cutting industry was Prague, where the St Wenceslas Chapel of the cathedral and the chapel of Karlstein Castle were decorated with large plates of cut and polished chrysoprase, agate and amethyst. At this time, too, the towns of Nuremberg and Strasbourg possessed gem-cutting industries. In 1405 the gem-cutters of Freiburg in the Black Forest formed a guild. Here, and in the neighbouring town of Waldkirch, a large variety of minerals, such as agate, chalcedony, rock-crystal and amethyst, were polished on revolving stone wheels driven by waterpower. This technique spread through the Saar towns northward to Idar and Oberstein in the Rhineland.

During the conquest of the New World fantastic riches in gemstones were brought to Europe. At royal courts and in the great trading cities, particularly in Spain, precious stones were much worn as personal adornments, and clothes, hats and shoes were often embellished with pearls, emeralds and other gemstones.

In the 17th century, at the height of the Baroque period, Zöblitz and Epinal in the Vosges district, as well as some of the princely courts, had groups of craftsmen who specialised in cutting and polishing marble and serpentine. There they made not only wall plates, pillars and baptismal fonts, but also bowls and ornate carvings. At the same time the cutting and polishing of indigenous garnets began to be an important industry in Bohemia, thus breaking the monopoly long held by the towns of the Black Forest. Lapidary centres using indigenous gemstones were also established in Silesia and Saxony.

89 TIFFANY DIAMOND. The world's largest and finest canary-yellow diamond ▪ Found 1871 in Africa, cut 1872 in Paris ▪ The diamond weighs 128.51 carats, and its present-day value is $ 544,500 ▪ 2½ in. × 2½ in. ▪ Tiffany, Jewellers, New York

After the beginning of the 19th century the importation of gemstones into Europe increased considerably. As a result, it was possible to establish lapidary centres in areas not dependent on local supplies of gemstones, as, for instance, in the Jura Mountains. This period also saw the rise of the gem-cutting industry in Paris and London.

The cutting and polishing of diamonds requires very special techniques. Diamonds were originally polished by rubbing two stones together, the technique being first introduced by Hungarian Jews to Amsterdam, Antwerp and Brussels. In 1467 the Dutchman Ludwig van Berquen discovered that diamonds can be polished with a powder of the same substance. As the Dutch succeeded just before 1600 in gaining a substantial foothold in the trade with India, and thus secured a large proportion of the diamonds coming from India to Europe over a period of two and a half centuries, they were able to ensure that Amsterdam, Antwerp and Bruges remained the leading diamond-cutting centres. Today, the diamond-cutting industry is concentrated in Antwerp, Amsterdam, Tel-Aviv—which is also one of the greatest diamond trading centres—and New York, and Hanau and Idar-Oberstein in West Germany.

New York houses the famous Tiffany Diamond, whose brilliance and unusual colour have been admired by New Yorkers and tourists for nearly 90 years. This golden stone was skilfully set by the famous artist and lapidary Jean Schlumberger into a diamond-studded brooch of gold and platinum (Plate 89).

In the course of the centuries, more than thirty distinct 'cuts' of gemstones have been developed. A characteristic feature of these cuts is that they give the stone a geometrically regular shape. This distinguishes them from the Indian cuts, which are very irregular. A major advance in the technique

of cutting took place when it was realised that the gemstone possesses definite optical properties which are related to its crystal symmetry. After that the facets of the stones were cut in the directions which would most effectively bring out these properties.

Gemstones have not only been used as ornaments, but from as far back in their history as we can go they have also been regarded by man as a repository of supernatural powers. In ancient Peru an emerald approaching the size of an ostrich egg was honoured as a god; and on the shores of the Nile there were statues made of lapis lazuli which were worshipped as the personifications of gods. Well-formed crystals of clear quartz were also worshipped in ancient times. Man has always believed in the power of amulets, and even today he often attributes special powers to gemstones. A polished plate of lapis lazuli with its included grains of pyrite was likened in the Orient to the starry heavens. For the inhabitants of Mesopotamia this was more than a pleasing comparison: since, in their eyes, all human destiny is controlled by the movement of the stars, it was inevitable that lapis lazuli should become a stone to which supernatural powers were attributed.

The early astrologers linked each of the then known planets with a day of the week, and the alchemists later connected these planets with certain minerals or metals. In this way the following relationships were established: Sunday–Sun, gold and sapphire; Monday–Moon, silver and rock-crystal; Tuesday–Mars, iron and diamond; Wednesday–Mercury, mercury and bloodstone; Thursday–Jupiter, tin and carnelian; Friday–Venus, copper and emerald; Saturday–Saturn, lead and onyx. There was also an astrological connection between the signs of the zodiac and certain gemstones, as follows: Ram–aquamarine, carnelian; Bull–hyacinth; Twins–chalcedony; Crab–emerald, Lion–topaz; Virgin–chrysolite; Balance–sardonyx; Scorpion–jasper, topaz; Archer–chrysoprase; Goat–ruby, onyx; Water-bearer–amethyst; Fishes–heliotrope, tourmaline. Once these stones of the zodiac were established, the so-called stones of the months soon followed. These were: January–garnet, hyacinth; February–amethyst; March–jasper, heliotrope, tourmaline; April–sapphire; May–agate; June–emerald, moonstone, chalcedony; July–onyx, sardonyx, ruby; August–carnelian, sard; September–chrysolite; October–aquamarine, beryl; November–topaz; December–chrysoprase, turquoise. These stones of the months were grouped in different ways by the various early communities. In all cases, however, they were supposed to endow the person born in that month with certain capabilities or to bestow on him good fortune. In the Anglo-Saxon world these stones of the months were supposed to be beneficial only to women or girls to whom they were presented.

The early writers tell us of the wonderful powers possessed by some gemstones. Pliny the Elder says of the diamond: 'It makes poisons impotent, drives off madness and dispels foolish fears...' Amethyst, according to the same source, is not only a safeguard against drunkenness; if one writes the name of the moon or sun on it and hangs it round one's neck with baboons' hairs or swallows' feathers, it protects one against sorcery, is helpful to those who have to deal with kings, and wards off hail and locusts.

Many of the ancient superstitions and some from Arabic sources were included in the lapidaries of the Middle Ages. We read, for instance, in the writings of Marbod of Rennes that: 'Agate protects from all bad poisons, even that of the viper. It quenches thirst and restores the eyesight. It protects the wearer, gives him strength and fresh colour, and, through the gift of fine speech, makes him well-liked of God and man.' Hildegard von Bingen gives the following advice: 'He who is ignorant through lack of all learning, but would like to acquire wisdom yet is incapable of doing so, but is not malicious and does not wish to become so, he should often rub his tongue with a sapphire, so that its warmth and strength, mixed with the warm moisture of the saliva, may dispel the noxious juices which oppress the intelligence and understanding in man. In this way a man may acquire a good intelligence.'

If we look at the many superstitions which man has woven around gemstones, only a few of which have been related here, we find that they are a sign of the rare charm which precious stones have exerted upon us. Pliny the Elder realised the secret of their charm and, with Latin clarity, formulated it as follows: 'In gemstones the whole majesty of Nature is compressed into the smallest space, and in a single stone we can perceive the masterpiece of creation.'

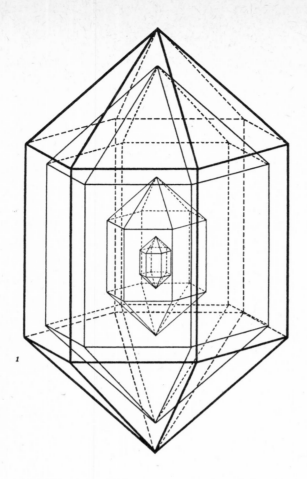

1

THE STRUCTURE AND GROWTH
OF CRYSTALS

ATOMIC STRUCTURE OF MINERALS. The constituent atoms of a crystal are arranged in a regular and recurring pattern which is known as the crystal lattice. The individual units —ions or atoms—are held in position by their electric charges (valencies). One of the minerals with the simplest crystal lattice is rock-salt, which is composed of positively charged ions of sodium and negatively charged ions of chlorine. Each Cl ion is surrounded by six equidistant Na ions, and conversely, each Na ion by six equidistant Cl ions.

The pattern of the individual atoms or ions in the crystal lattice determines the lattice type of the mineral. The size of individual ions and their distance from one another varies with each mineral. Graphite, for instance, forms a lattice type composed of superimposed layers of ions.

Fig. 1 Crystal growth by deposition of parallel layers of crystalline substance. Stages in the growth of a quartz crystal.

Fig. 2 Crystal lattice of rock-salt. Equidistant ions of Na and Cl.

Fig. 3 Crystal lattice of graphite. Layers of hexagonal rings of carbon atoms, with distance between layers of atoms greater than that between atoms within the layer. The layered structure explains the perfect cleavage of graphite.

CRYSTAL FACES, EDGES AND SOLID ANGLES. Minerals often form well-developed crystals bounded by flat faces and straight edges. However, a crystalline body does not necessarily have a well-defined external form. The relationship between the number of faces (F), edges (E) and solid angles (A) of a crystal can be expressed by the formula: $F + A = E + 2$.

CRYSTAL GROWTH. Crystals grow by the deposition of parallel layers of the same substance on the faces of the embryonic crystal. This growth may take place by sublimation from the gaseous phase, by deposition from aqueous solutions or magmatic melts, or by exchange of material in the solid state. If the supply of material during crystal growth is uneven, distorted crystals will be formed. The faces of distorted crystals may be of very different size from the equivalent faces of perfect crystals, but the angles between equivalent faces in perfect and distorted crystals are the same.

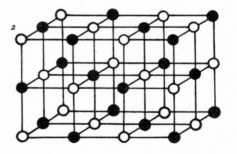

2

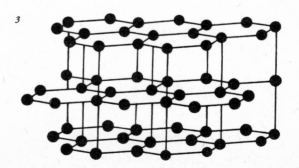

3

184

SYMMETRY OF CRYSTALS. The many crystal forms can be grouped according to their elements of symmetry into six crystal systems.

The axes of symmetry of most crystals are such that the crystal faces at both their ends are arranged in the same way. In certain crystals, however, the faces at opposite ends of an axis are different. Crystals with such polar axes of symmetry—the so-called hemimorphic crystals—thus have dissimilar faces at either end and possess quite distinctive physical and pyro-electric properties.

On the basis of their external symmetry, all possible crystal forms fall into 32 classes of symmetry. Every mineral species, however, crystallises in only one of these classes. An understanding of the symmetry of crystal systems can best be gained by studying the relationship of their crystal axes.

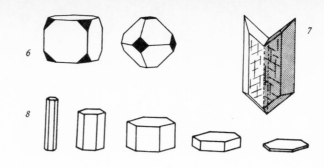

Fig. 6 Combination of cube and octahedron in galena. Left: crystal with cubic habit (faces of octahedron black). Right: crystal of octahedral habit (faces of cube black).

Fig. 7 Twinned crystal of gypsum, the so-called swallow-tail twin; one individual crystal is dotted. The re-entrant angle at the top is a characteristic feature of twinned crystals.

Fig. 8 Various habits of the same crystal form, i.e. hexagonal prism: long columnar, prismatic, isometric, tabular, platy.

CRYSTAL SYSTEMS, LENGTHS AND ANGULAR RELATIONSHIP OF AXES:

Cubic	3 axes of equal length intersecting at right angles.
Tetragonal	3 axes; vertical axis of different length from the two horizontal axes; all at right angles.
Hexagonal	4 axes; three equal and horizontal, making angles of 120° with each other; vertical axis at right angles to plane of horizontal axes and of different length.
Orthorhombic	3 axes; all unequal and all at right angles.
Monoclinic	3 axes; all unequal, one axis at right angles to the vertical axis, the third at an oblique angle to the other two.
Triclinic	3 axes; all unequal and none at right angles.

TWINS. Crystals are many-sided convex bodies, designed to fill space to best advantage. Re-entrant angles are thus only found in regular crystal intergrowths known as twins.

CRYSTAL SYSTEM AND HABIT. The number and positioning of all faces which bound a crystal determine its crystal system. The habit of a crystal, however, is determined by the relative sizes of the various faces, i.e. its general shape.

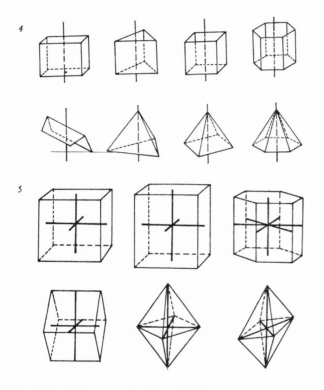

Fig. 4 Axes of symmetry, left to right: 2-fold, 3-fold, 4-fold and 6-fold. Upper row: holohedral forms; lower row: hemimorphic forms with polar axes.

Fig. 5 Arrangement of axes in the six crystal systems:
cubic   tetragonal   hexagonal
orthorhombic   monoclinic   triclinic

185

BIBLIOGRAPHY

Minerals

BERRY, L. G., and MASON, B., 1959. Mineralogy, Concepts, Descriptions, Determinations. W. H. Freeman, San Francisco.

BÖRNER, R., 1962. Minerals, Rocks and Gemstones. Oliver and Boyd, Edinburgh and London.

DEER, W. A., HOWIE, R. A., and ZUSSMAN, J., 1962–63. Rock Forming Minerals. 5 vols. Longmans, London.

FORD, W. E., 1951. Dana's Textbook of Mineralogy, 4th ed. John Wiley, New York; Chapman and Hall, London.

GLEASON, S., 1960. Ultraviolet Guide to Minerals. Van Nostrand Co., New York.

HEINRICH, E.W., 1958. Mineralogy and Geology of Radioactive Raw Materials. McGraw-Hill, New York.

JONES, W. R., 1943. Minerals in Industry. Penguin Books, Harmondsworth.

—— and WILLIAMS, D., 1954. Minerals and Mineral Deposits. Oxford University Press.

KERR, P. F., 1959. Optical Mineralogy. 3rd ed. McGraw-Hill, New York.

KIRKALDY, J. F., 1963. Minerals and Rocks in Colour. Blandford Press, London.

PALACHE, C. H., BERMAN, H., and FRONDEL, C., 1944–62. Dana's System of Mineralogy. 7th ed. 3 vols. John Wiley, New York; Chapman and Hall, London.

READ, H. H., 1962. Rutley's Elements of Mineralogy. 25th ed. Murby, London.

ROGERS, A. F., 1937. Introduction to the Study of Minerals. McGraw-Hill, New York.

SMITH, H. G., 1956. Minerals and the Microscope. 4th ed. revised by M. K. Wells. Murby, London.

WAHLSTROM, E. E., 1955. Petrographic Mineralogy. John Wiley, New York; Chapman and Hall, London.

WINCHELL, A. N., 1961. Elements of Optical Mineralogy. 3 vols. John Wiley, New York; Chapman and Hall, London.

Crystallography

BURGER, U. J., 1956. Elementary Crystallography. John Wiley, New York.

PHILLIPS, F. C., 1963. An Introduction to Crystallography. 3rd ed. Longmans, London.

WAHLSTROM, E. E., 1949. Optical Crystallography. John Wiley, New York; Chapman and Hall, London.

WOLFE, C. W., 1953. Manual for Geometrical Crystallography. Edwards, Ann Arbor, Michigan.

Gemstones

ANDERSON, B.W., 1958. Gem Testing. 6th ed. Heywood, London.

KRAUS, E. H., and SLAWSON, C. B., 1957. Gems and Gem Materials. 5th ed. McGraw-Hill, New York.

McLINTOCK, W. F. P., 1951. A Guide to the Collection of Gemstones in the Geological Museum. 3rd ed., revised by P. A. Sabine. Geological Survey and Museum. (H.M.S.O.)

SINKANKS, J., 1961. Gemstones and Minerals—how and where to find them. Van Nostrand, New York.

SMITH, G. F. HERBERT, 1958. Gem Stones, 13th ed., revised by Coles Phillips. Methuen, London.

SPENCER, L. J., 1946. A Key to Precious Stones. Blackie, Glasgow and London.

WEBSTER, R., 1957. Practical Gemmology. 3rd ed. N.A.G. Press, London.

Rocks

BARTH, T. F. W., 1952. Theoretical Petrology. A Textbook on the Origin and Evolution of Rocks. John Wiley, New York; Chapman and Hall, London.

GROUT, F. F. Petrography and Petrology, 1932. McGraw-Hill, New York.

HARKER, A., 1950. Metamorphism. 3rd ed. Methuen, London.

—— 1960. Petrology for Students. 8th ed., revised by C. E. Tilley, S. R. Nocholds and M. Black. Cambridge University Press.

HATCH, F. H., RASTALL, R. H., and BLACK, M., 1950. The Petrology of the Sedimentary Rocks. Murby, London.

HATCH, F. H., WELLS, A. K., and WELLS, M. K., 1961. The Petrology of the Igneous Rock. 12th ed. Murby, London.

PETTIJOHN, F. J., 1957. Sedimentary Rocks. 2nd ed. Harper, New York.

RAMBERG, H., 1958. The Origin of Metamorphic and Metasomatic Rocks. 2nd ed. Univ. of Chicago Press, Chicago.

SHAND, S. J., 1947. Eruptive Rocks. 3rd ed. John Wiley, New York.

TURNER, F. J., and VERHOOGEN, J., 1960. Igneous and Metamorphic Petrology. 2nd ed. McGraw-Hill, New York.

TYRRELL, G. W., 1950. The Principles of Petrology. 11th ed. Methuen, London.

WILLIAMS, H., TURNER, F. J., and GILBERT, C. M., 1958. Petrography, an Introduction to the Study of Rocks in Thin Section. W. H. Freeman, San Francisco.

Mineral Deposits and Geochemistry

BATEMAN, A. M., 1951. The Formation of Mineral Deposits. John Wiley, New York; Chapman and Hall, London.

LINDGREN, W., 1953. Mineral Deposits. 4th ed. McGraw-Hill, New York and London.

MASON, B., 1958. Principles of Geochemistry. 2nd ed. John Wiley, New York; Chapman and Hall, London.

NIGGLI, P., 1954. Rocks and Mineral Deposits. W. H. Freeman, San Francisco.

RANKAMA, K., and SAHAMA, T. G., 1950. Geochemistry. University of Chicago Press, Chicago.

VOSKULL, W. H., 1955. Minerals in World Industry. McGraw-Hill, New York.

Meteorites

MASON, B., 1962. Meteorites. John Wiley, New York.

Dictionaries

CHALLINOR, J., 1962. A Dictionary of Geology. University of Wales Press.

Chambers's Mineralogical Dictionary, 1948.

INDEX

Figures set in roman type indicate page numbers;
those in italic refer to plate numbers

189